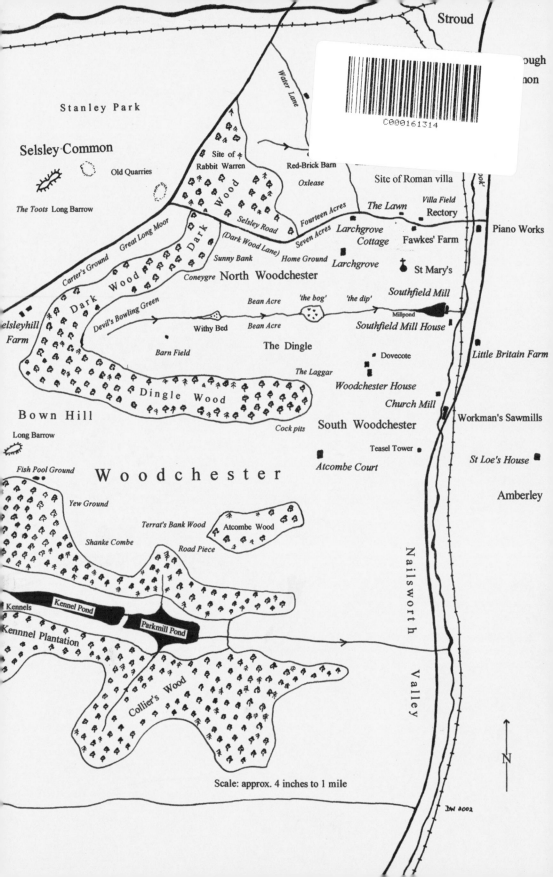

Hunters of Longtree

Hunters of Longtree

A Cotswold Tale

by David Walker

with wood engravings by the author

For Vera
Best wishes
David 29. 8. 2003

ORPHEUS
PRESS

Copyright © David Walker 2003
Illustrations © David Walker 2003
First published in 2003 by Orpheus Press
4 Walmer Meadow
Aldridge, West Midlands WS9 8QQ

Distributed by Gazelle Book Services Limited
Falcon House, Queen Square
Lancaster, England LA1 1RN

British Library Cataloguing in Publication Data
A catalogue record for this book is available from the British Library

ISBN 0-9540366-0-3

Typeset by Amolibros, Watchet, Somerset
This book production has been managed by Amolibros
Printed and bound by T J International Ltd, Padstow, Cornwall

For George, Archie and Zak, who one day may discover the secrets of Longtree, and to the memory of my parents and my aunt who enabled me to know those same secrets

The Stoat

Stealing stealthily through the tussocks,
Spurning warning cries of ruddocks,
White-gloved paws softly treading,
Supple spine like spring steel spreading,
Black tail tassel faintly flicking,
Brown velvet ears each one way twitching,
Long white whiskers the grass blades brushing;
Scent of stoat the meadow mouse hushing.

Rattle of ruddocks at last relenting,
Warm moist nostrils forever scenting;
Sense the she stoat stepping lightly,
Blackberry eyes gleaming brightly.
Meadow mouse, the grass stalks cropping,
Crams each cheek pouch without stopping;
Russet rodent in form sits shivering,
Finely whiskered muzzle quivering.

Stoat hears sound of small teeth grating;
For chance to strike she's eagerly waiting.
The meadow mouse, not yet sated,
Stands its ground, its short life fated.
Now see the she stoat sprightly springing;
To victim's nape her claws are clinging,
In the manner of a cat—
Itaque sanguis terminat.

DW

Introduction

Hunters of Longtree is the product of a lifelong affection for a region of the South Cotswolds, combined with a fascination for the lives of predatory mammals such as stoats and weasels, which began almost forty years ago while identifying the prey of these predators by the microscopic examination of hairs and feathers in their stomachs and droppings. During my time as a natural history museum curator and biology teacher I was fortunate to be able to pursue this line of study, particularly of that most elusive of predators, the stoat. Such an opportunity would not have been possible without the co-operation of a number of land owners, and especially their gamekeepers, most of whom would have put many a graduate biologist to shame by their breadth of knowledge and concern for the welfare of the countryside and its tenants.

The book is intended to be a sort of 'ecological reconstruction' in that it encompasses the relationships between plants and animals, including man, and their environment, in a specific area of the South Cotswolds, namely Woodchester, near Stroud in Gloucestershire. The 'hunters' are principally a family of stoats, the 'royal hunters' of the Gloucestershire Cotswolds, but may equally stand for the local teenage boys who interact with their recent post-war rural environment. Through the senses of the stoat and the many other predators, as much as through the boys', the reader is taken on a tour of Longtree to experience, often in the most intimate detail, the inter-relationships of its wildlife as well as the passage of human history. I have used the elusive stoat both as a symbol and a main character in the real-life nature drama, 'red in tooth and claw', which is constantly being enacted in the countryside and from which, sadly, most of us have become alienated.

In a sense I have tried to compose a 'recollection of the Cotswold countryside', portraying a landscape of fifty years ago, relatively untouched by intensive farming and supporting a greater diversity of wildlife. Then children of my generation could walk along the lanes without fear of being abducted or explore the fields, woods and commons and collect birds' eggs or butterflies, unhindered by overzealous or misguided conservationists.

Over the last twenty-five years I have made countless seasonal visits to Woodchester to make observations and record on film the countryside I first became acquainted with as an infant evacuee from London during the Blitz, living with an aunt and uncle, and later through the relatively undiscerning eyes of a young teenager during school holidays. While researching the natural history of Woodchester and neighbouring parishes in Longtree Hundred, I became equally intrigued by the evidence of human history, from Stone Age long barrows, Iron Age hill forts and Roman villas through to medieval manor and land use during the last two centuries. This ingredient of the narrative I have used to temper the often necessary bloodthirsty descriptions of scenes provided by the stoat's and other predators' hunting habits.

In the early 1950s, when rabbits were abundant, and only a few years before myxomatosis decimated their numbers, I have vivid recollections of watching stoats hunting over the warrens of Woodchester. The burgeoning rabbit population in spring provided easy prey for badgers, which had not yet been harassed on suspicion of transmitting TB to cattle. At this time Fawkes' farm was at the hub of the village, its mixed dairy herd supplying milk and the land it farmed providing pasture, hay, lucerne and root crops to feed the cows throughout the year. There was also a bakery that baked bread and cakes in a coke-fired oven. These features gave a stability and vitality to this almost self-sufficient community, as yet untainted by the culture of consumerism that was to follow. It was the period in which I prefer to remember Woodchester, with some nostalgia, and is partly the reason I have chosen to set the book at this time, which was also when I began to take a real interest in the natural world.

In creating this piece of writing I feel I am sharing with readers a privileged knowledge of the countryside. I hope it will make them aware of the satisfaction to be gained from concentrating the senses and taking the 'time to stand and stare', as W H Davies the tramp poet, who lived in the same valley as Woodchester, reminds us through his popular poem 'Leisure'. In this fast age where we are often cut off from the sights and sounds of the countryside by our speeding cars, and our ears are assaulted by personal stereos, mobile phones and car alarms, we are losing the facility to tune in to Nature. Perhaps it will also help us to realise the value of a more measured, less materialistic way of life that is synonymous with true country living.

During the book's long gestation I have received help and encouragement from many people. I am particularly grateful to the following: Professor F W Rogers Brambell DSc FRS, former Professor of Zoology at the University of Wales, Bangor; Peter Hanney MSc FMA FRES former Keeper of Natural History at Birmingham Museum; Dr H N Southern, formerly of the Animal Ecology Research Group, Zoology Department, Oxford University; Dr Chris O'Toole of the Oxford University Museum; Dr E G Neal; S H Jervis-Read CBE MC of the Game Farmers' Association; The Earl of Aylesford at Packington Park and his keeper Sq Ldr J L Brown DFC; Lord Brocket of Brocket Park and his keepers Messrs Rodgers and Haywood; Charles Hambro and his keeper Brian Wells on the Dumbleton estate.

For help with understanding the archaeology, local history and geology of the area, I am indebted to the Archaeology and Social History Departments at Birmingham Museum; Brian S Smith MA FSA, County Archivist at Gloucester Records Office; Catherine Johns BA FSA of the British Museum; Lionel Walrond FMA FSA former Curator of Stroud Museum; Dr Della Hooke and Professor C C Dyer of Birmingham University, also Dr C Cox, for help with interpreting the Anglo-Saxon charters of Woodchester; Dr R Sanderson of the Geological Museum London and Ian Standing of the Dean Heritage Trust, for help with the provenance of local building stone.

Over the years a number of Woodchester inhabitants, some of whom remembered the 1950s, have kindly shared their memories and provided invaluable information about the local history of the area. I thank the following: my brothers, Duncan, Brian and George; Dick Townsend; Mrs J Hammond; Mrs Parnell; William Brunt; David Gazzard; Derek Dalby; Agnes Tite of Larchgrove, for her fine observations of badgers in the garden, and her gardener Maurice Niblett; Colin and Kathy Tite; Miriam Kelly, formerly of the Field Centre at Woodchester Park; Woodchester local historian Neville Crawford and his widow Doreen; Edward Payne, for knowledge of his mother's natural history painting activities; Charles Stuart-Menteth of Woodchester House; Eddy Price of Frocester Court Farm. I am especially grateful to my wise octogenarian friends Lance Cordwell and Sturdee Click, who have given so generously of their priceless country lore on my numerous welcoming visits.

For sharing with me their unique knowledge of the science and craft of foxhunting, and for tolerating my close presence in the hunting field on several occasions, I thank Mr R J Berkeley, former Master of the Berkeley Hunt; Bob Blake, present Master of the Berkeley Hunt; Tim Langley, its former huntsman; Chris Maiden, present huntsman; Alan Underwood, former hon sec; Tim Unwin, former Master of the Cotswold Hunt; A H Villiers of the Old Priory.

I thank Birmingham Central Reference Library for arranging

inter-library loans and for making available, over a period of four years, every issue of *The Field* that has been published from 1853 to 1993. Here I found in 'Letters to the Editor' a wealth of information on the behaviour of the stoat, much of which corroborated my own observations and those of other naturalists and gamekeepers. I had first discovered such correspondence in the collections of the Natural History Department at Birmingham Museum under 'Scrapbooks of British Mammals' compiled by Birmingham solicitor and amateur naturalist J L Auden MC, first cousin of W H Auden.

Special thanks go to Elizabeth Sargeant and Nick Vlismas for battling with the draft manuscript and for making constructive comments. I am equally grateful to the following people for reading the manuscript and providing reviews: Simon Hart, Director of the Countryside Alliance's Campaign for Hunting; Mr R J Berkeley of Berkeley Castle; Owen Wade CBE MD FRCP, former Vice-Principal of Birmingham University and Dean of the Medical School. For permission to reproduce the wood engraving of a stoat, I acknowledge the estate of C F Tunnicliffe RA 1980. For producing computer images of the illustrations, I thank SMK Studio, Aldridge, and my son-in-law David Farmer. And I am sincerely grateful to my old friend Dr Jan Tieken of Leeuwarden, Friesland, for his generous support with this venture. I thank Jane Tatam of Amolibros for so expertly seeing the book through to production. Last but not least, I am grateful to my wife Susan without whose constant encouragement my work would never have seen the light of day. She helped me endure its painful parturition after a protracted gestation.

Sunrise over Longtree

I

The April sun rose above the edge of the wold and shone across the steep-sided valley on to the opposite hillside, setting ablaze the gilded weathercock on its lofty steeple perch. Noisy jackdaws flocked around the church spire, some carrying elm twigs in their bills to repair the nests that past generations of birds had built within its dark recesses. The church clock chimed seven, and in the mild south-westerly breeze the golden cockerel surveyed the South Cotswold parish of Woodchester, which lay in the hundred of Longtree. The hundred is said to have derived its name from a tall tree, which in Anglo-Saxon times stood in the neighbouring parish of Avening and under which the men of the tithing held their council. It is also said that here Earl Godwin, who had land in the hundred, and his sons, Swein and Harold, gathered their armies to fight Edward the Confessor in 1052. Several centuries before the Saxons settled, after the Roman invasion, two of Emperor Claudius's generals, Ostorius Scapula and Vespasian, are supposed to have ordered the building of certain

1

public works in the neighbourhood, and this is how Woodchester got its name, which means 'Roman camp in the wood'.

Sunlight flooded a wood at the head of a small combe in the north of the parish. The beech wood, through which ran the northern boundary of Woodchester, was called Dark Wood, which had grown up on an ancient rabbit warren. A tawny owl hooted and huddled closer to an ivy-clad beech bole to try to escape the attention of mobbing titmice. Around the tree's spreading roots lay pellets composed of the fur and bones of wood mice, which the owl had caught during the night. In a burrow beneath the roots a dog stoat stirred from his sleep. Sensing the warm sunshine outside, he crawled along the short tunnel to the entrance and cautiously peered out through bright, black eyes. This royal hunter, as the stoat is known in some parts of the wold, we will call Aethelwald, which in the language of the Anglo-Saxons means 'noble and famous one'.

Aethelwald emerged from his den and stretched his stiff muscles. His handsome, wedge-shaped head and long muscular neck and back were covered with rich reddish-brown fur. His elegant tail was a third the length of his body and bore a tuft of long black hairs. Along his flanks the fine, dense, buff-coloured underfur showed through the coarser, brown guard hairs of the outerfur. His underparts, from chin to loins and along the insides of his short sturdy limbs, were creamy white with a tint of lemon. The tip of his broad muzzle bore two small white flashes, and from its sides sprouted long brown and white whiskers, or vibrissae. The same kind of whiskers, but shorter, stood erect above his eyebrows, beneath which his dark, piercing eyes shone like ripe elderberries. His alert, forward-pointing ears were covered with short velvety hairs and were outlined in white. His broad, powerful paws were clothed with white hairs, which concealed sabre-sharp claws projecting from fur-lined, deep-cleft pads. He was indeed a noble-looking royal hunter.

Like other dog stoats, Aethelwald had roamed far and wide throughout these southern parts of the wold, and like many of his forebears he had been born on a wooded estate several miles to the south of Woodchester, where the wold gave way to the wide vale. In his first spring, his wandering instinct was aroused, and he left his birthplace as the golden celandines began to bloom. He travelled northwards along hedgerow and drystone wall, brook course and woodland edge, crossing cart track and metalled road, till he reached a steep-sided wooded valley in the south of the parish called Woodchester Park. Here he wandered widely in search of prey and mates, and in defence of his domain. In his second spring, he left the park and crossed Bown Hill into the northern part of the parish. In his new domain, through spring and high summer, he wooed several bitch stoats and sired their young. Now, in his third spring, he frequented land in North Woodchester.

He followed one of his regular hunting routes along the edge of Dark Wood, keeping close to the drystone wall that enclosed it. The buttress-like roots of beeches drew their nourishment from the thin soil and from the underlying limestone that had been laid down in a warm, shallow sea one hundred million years ago. In this sea, myriad corals, molluscs, fish and their reptilian predators had flourished, and on its sandy shores had walked flesh-eating dinosaurs. The same bedrock underlay every hill and hanger, holding in its stony grasp remnants of but a few of these prehistoric creatures.

As he crossed a track used by woodmen and rabbit catchers, a pair of tomtits spied him and gave their scolding cries from a beech bough stump in which they had their nest. Six summers past, the rotten branch had broken off close to the grey-barked bole, and winter rains had hastened the stump's decay. Over the past week, the industrious blue tits had pecked out a short tunnel and smooth-walled nest chamber from the rotten heartwood. The amount of chippings the pair had removed was equal to many times the bulk of their tiny bodies. Although the nest hole was only just wide enough to allow the birds' passage, both the slender stoat and weasel could find their way in. The previous year a bitch stoat had plundered a nest in a neighbouring tree that had since been felled. Fear of these small members of the weasel tribe had long been instilled in the blue tit's tiny head, and in dread the pair watched until the royal hunter had disappeared from their sight.

Aethelwald stopped in his tracks and sat up on his hindlegs. He cocked his head into the wind and scented the mild, moist air. He could smell the rabbits that were feeding out in the nine-acre pasture known as Oxlease, for the wind had veered to the south-east and carried their scent into the wood through a breach in the tumbledown wall. He climbed over the few remaining courses of stone and ran into the cover of a bramble brake. The ground smelled strongly of fox.

Emerging from the brambles, he stood retriever-like, his nose pointing towards the spot where four half-grown rabbits cropped the lush spring grass. He hid behind a tussock, watching them as they grazed. One of them stopped feeding and sat upright, its head turned towards the wood. It held its well-groomed paws limply against its white chest, its quivering nostrils constantly sampling the air, and, sensing no danger, it lowered its head to graze again.

A second rabbit bounded a few paces and squatted down once more to feed, its ears held flat along its back. A third rabbit followed. Aethelwald watched its white scut bobbing as it ran, and, with a flick of his tail tag, he broke cover. As he gave chase in strong leaps and bounds, all four rabbits scattered widely. The one he had singled out ran into a bramble thicket, and finding itself on unfamiliar ground became confused and scuttled out again. It began to run at a slower pace with its ears laid back, and with his muzzle held close to the ground, Aethelwald followed hard on its heels. He came out of the brambles and eagerly scented the rabbit-trodden turf. So keen was his nose that only once did he overrun the rabbit's line. Many times he had given chase to rabbits with a good deal more spirit in them than this one showed.

The rabbit began to run an erratic path over the field, its pace slowing even more, till finally it came to rest close to the drystone wall, and, crouching low in the grass, it gave out a high-pitched squeal. A farm labourer heard the unmistakable cry of the stoated rabbit, but he knew he would not be able to pick up the prize before the royal hunter claimed it. It lay still, trembling, its heart racing and its eyes glazed over. The breeze parted the hairs of its soft young pelt, exposing the downy, blue-grey underfur of its rump. Aethelwald soon caught up with his prey as it lay squealing in the grass, transfixed by the nearness of its pursuer.

Although the exhausted creature could see its enemy, it made no attempt to escape, as though resigned to its imminent fate. Aethelwald lunged at the rabbit, embracing its forequarters with his outstretched forepaws. He bit into the side of its neck, and with his hindlegs raked backwards over its shuddering flanks. Though his canine teeth had become blunted through biting on bone, his jaw muscles were just as powerful, so death came swiftly to the young rabbit. He gripped his quarry until the heart ceased to pump. Drops of blood, rosehip red, oozed from the puncture wounds made by his canines and trickled over the short ochreous fur of the rabbit's skinny neck. He licked up the warm savoury fluid till it flowed no more.

Aethelwald looked furtively about him, but did not see the dog fox watching from the edge of the wood. He walked round the dead rabbit and took hold of it in his jaws by the nape, and, bracing his powerful neck and shoulder muscles, he lifted the limp forequarters and dragged the body, equivalent to more than one and a half times his own weight, along the ground, stopping now and then to rest and renew his hold.

Knowing the location of all the rabbit burrows in the warren, he soon found one in which to secrete his kill, and, backing into the entrance, he pulled it out of sight. For a while, he lay quietly to recover from his exertions, then began to eat the rabbit in the seclusion of the disused burrow. By the time he had consumed the brain and most of the forequarters, the three rabbits that had escaped their companion's fate were out feeding again in Oxlease with others from the warren. He knew too which parts of the warren provided the choicest rabbits, for he preferred young animals whose flesh was the most tender. Woodman and farm labourer alike knew that any rabbit he could pick up would always be a clean and healthy animal that would skin well and provide sweet meat for the pot.

Aethelwald curled up in his earthy refuge, close to the remains of the rabbit's chilling corpse. His body formed a furry elipse, with his head tucked into his cream-coloured loins, white chin uppermost. The edge of one ear bore a notch, which marked an old wound he had received during his first spring as a yearling, when he had fought with an older dog stoat. As he dozed, he made tiny warbling sounds, and his pelt twitched and rippled as the muscles relaxed and recharged themselves. One might even imagine he was dreaming of some past adventure of courtship or the chase.

In human history, during the reign of Alfred the Great, there lived a Saxon thane called Aethelwald who held all the woodland on the estate of Woodchester. A century and a half before Alfred's time, King Aethelbald of Mercia had granted the woodland to the See of Worcester, in the name of Bishop Wilfrid. In the first charter of Woodchester he had set down the bounds of the estate, which had formerly belonged to the Romans, and before them to an Iron Age tribe known as the Dobunni.

In response to a complaint from Bishop Werferth of Worcester that Aethelwald had deprived him of certain woodlands (meaning he had not been giving the bishop his rightful share in the profits of their management), Alfred instructed his son-in-law, Duke Aethelred, to hold a Witan, or court of enquiry, at Gloucester to hear the case. At the Witan a compromise was reached whereby Aethelwald and his son, Alhmund, were granted the lease of the woodland for the duration of their lives, with the exception of some swine pasturage at a place called Long Ridge. Thereafter the property was to revert to the See of Worcester. It was also agreed that Aethelwald's agent, Ecglaf, should ride with Wulphun, the bishop's chaplain, to check the bounds of the estate as they had been set down in the charter.

So the two men set off on horseback from Gloucester to ride round Woodchester tracing the bounds, Wulphun reading them out from the old deeds. First, they came to Guinnethleah, or the lea of the water-meeting, where the tributaries of the Frome come together. Then they climbed the limestone hill called Roddanbeorg to the north. From here, they rode over the hilltops and along the heads of the combes on the east, from where they could look down on the estate. Next, they came to Smiececumb, or the misty combe, then to Sengedleah, or the burnt lea. From here they rode to Heardenleah, or hard and dry lea, and then on to Lesser Naeglesleah in the south. Then they travelled along Widancumb in Carlesleah on the west and on to Haeslburg, or hazel barrow, then to Haboccumb, or hawk's combe, ending up at Aethelferth's ploughland. Although the exact route the Saxons took and many of the places named in the charter have eluded scholars of human history, the whole of the former ancient estate of Woodchester would have been well known to the ancestors of Aethelwald our royal hunter.

The chimes of the church clock told the passing of three quarters of another hour, and almost four since Aethelwald had set out on his first foray of the day. Now the sun was approaching its zenith in the southern sky and shone over the whole parish. In Oxlease, cows were replenishing their stomachs with the rich spring grass. Oxlease was bordered on the east by Water Lane. Better known to the local inhabitants as Watery Lane, a constant stream of water trickled down its steep northern end, from an overflowing stone trough set in the bank and supplied by a spring.

On the opposite side of the lane lay another meadow, named Shortcombe, known to some of the locals as Shurcomb, along whose marshy margin ran a stream, fed by another spring, and which marked the continuation of the parish's northern boundary. The stream flowed into an old millpond, and the remains of the small millstream that ran from it, which used to drive the wheel of a gigmill for raising the nap on woollen cloth, meandered through a spinney. It then joined a wider stream, known locally as 'the brook', which flowed northwards along the valley to join the Frome at Stroud, and into which the tail races of many mills once flowed. The brook formed Woodchester's eastern boundary.

The northern margin of the millpond was fringed with trees and dense undergrowth, and was a haven for wildlife. All was still, save for the crooning of a culver, or woodpigeon, in a larch, and the loud croaking 'curruc' of a moorhen on the millpond. Then from the undergrowth came the strident piping call of a cock blackbird, followed by the warning cries of robin and wren. Halfway up an ivy-clad alder appeared the cause of the birds' alarm calls. It was another royal hunter, a bitch stoat, whom we will call Gytha. She was half the size of the dog stoat Aethelwald, being little longer than the flower spikes of the reedmace, which in late summer grew at the western edge of the pond.

As Gytha moved into a patch of sunlight, the russet hairs of her sleek body glinted like burnished copper, and her underparts were the colour of elder blossom. In her jaws, she carried a neat bundle of dried grass. With the needle-sharp claws and tiny pads of her white-gloved paws she gripped the furrowed bark and climbed up to her den. Despite being heavy with young, she was as agile at climbing trees as her close relative, the bushy-tailed marten, which was hunted for its fine fur in Woodchester's woods during Roman and Anglo-Saxon times. The ease with which she reached the tree hole could only be equalled by the grey squirrel, which was now so common in the woods. After she had climbed into her den, the birds' cries subsided. Over the past week, she had made the tree hole her main refuge, for she knew it was a safe place to have her young.

In her first summer, while still a kitten in the nest, Gytha had been impregnated by Aethelwald, on whose domain her mother

The author in Dark Wood ('Rabbit Warren Wood)
about 1942? age 5 yrs! Taken by Duncan.

lived. Throughout the waxing and waning of ten moons she carried in her womb the dormant germs of seven new lives. As the hazel catkins in Watery Lane shed their pollen in the early March winds, the embryos became implanted, and by the time the first chiffchaff arrived in the parish, seven tiny hearts began to beat in her belly.

She laid down the bundle of dried grass in the tree hollow, on top of what she had already collected, and holding it down with her forepaws she teased out the pliant stems with her chisel-shaped incisor teeth. Then with her muzzle and paws she moulded them into a nest. Nearby lay the headless, partly eaten body of a three-week-old rabbit. With the same teeth she plucked the soft fur from the rabbit's rump and worked it into the nest, using an innate skill that went back millions of years through the royal hunter's long lineage.

Gytha ranged over a far smaller portion of the parish than the dog stoat whose young she carried. She had been born beneath the roots of an oak growing by the brook, and throughout the year of her birth she explored the length of the brook with its withy beds, venturing into neighbouring Selsley. Here she became familiar with all the small meadows and their hedgerows and the railway embankment running parallel with the brook. Though during the summer she travelled with her mother and siblings to more distant woods and warrens, by the autumn she had become independent and returned to her birthplace. During the hard winter, she sought shelter in a barn at Waterlane Farm, where she hunted rats and mice.

In the annals of Domesday it is written that, during the reign of Hardicanute, the estate of Woodchester passed by purchase from Azor to Earl Godwin of Kent, a Saxon of great ability and power who virtually ruled the kingdom of Wessex. Godwin, who lived at Berkeley in the vale, gave Woodchester to his Danish princess Gytha, mother of King Harold, for it is written that she was 'unwilling to consume anything from the manor of Berkeley on account of the destruction of the abbey there', in which Godwin is said to have had a share. It is also said that in order to procure the abbey lands, he set his handsome nephew to seduce the beautiful abbess and many of the nuns. Then he complained of their misconduct to King Edward, who therefore granted their property to the earl. It is even said by some that Gytha founded a religious house at Woodchester on the site of the Roman villa, using the stone, bricks and tiles from its ruins. Such sayings show that human history, unlike natural history, is often illusive. Likewise, the alleged misdeeds and depredations of Saxon thane and nobleman cannot be compared to the natural predatory habits of the elusive royal hunter and the other creatures revealed within these pages.

Trough in Watery Lane

II

One by one, the lights of the houses on the hillside that the Saxons called Roddanbeorg went out like sparks from a dying autumn bonfire. The moon cast its feeble light over the parish. A lone barn owl flew the length of Shortcombe meadow to the stream that flowed into the old millpond. Like some gargantuan white moth, the silent hunter quartered the marshy ground bordering the stream. Its soft wing feathers made no perceptible sound as they beat the air, and were not even heard by a shrew as it ventured out into the dewy grass to gobble an earthworm. With wings outstretched and talons splayed, the owl soon silenced the noisy predator before it could finish its meal. From its gatepost perch, the owl heard a badger scramble up the bank of Watery Lane. The aged boar, who lived alone in a set below Dark Wood, didn't notice the owl take flight and glide in front of his snuffling nose as he lumbered along one of his regular tracks through the field known as Hunger Hill, in neighbouring Selsley.

In her den in the alder tree hollow, Gytha felt her young stir within her, and once more she licked the tight tender skin of her swollen belly. Over the last few days she had spent more time sleeping, feeding from the remains of a rabbit, and adding some of its fur to the nest. She winced at the birth pangs rippling through her belly, and she moved round in the nest to try to find relief from her pain. She lay in a half-moon posture and dozed for as long as it took the old badger to dig up a nest of baby rabbits from the railway embankment. Once more, she circled the nest to ease the spasms, and, lying on her side, she kneaded her throbbing belly with firm strokes of her tongue. She crouched with one hindleg slightly raised, and, sitting on the other haunch, she reached over and groomed the cream hairs covering her belly. She licked the moist and swollen entrance to her birth canal, and in the time it took the barn owl to swallow another shrew, she gave birth to her first kitten.

In the darkness of her den she nuzzled and licked her firstborn. She bit through and licked off the transparent membranes that enveloped it, and as she tenderly massaged its wet body with her tongue, she felt it take its first breath. She ate the blood-filled afterbirth and chewed the cord that had been its lifeline, severing it close to its bloated body. The kitten was barely larger than a filbertnut, coral-pink and sparsely covered with short white hairs, as delicate and downy as those growing along the edge of a young beech leaf when it has just burst from its winter bud in May. It lay on its back squirming, its tiny feet pawing the air, until it righted itself. Slowly it crawled over the nest, rolling its rotund head from side to side, its primitive senses responding to the warmth and odour of its mother's body. As Gytha braced herself for the next delivery, she felt the kitten nuzzle her warm belly, and, finding one of her moist nipples, it took hold and sucked hard between tongue and toothless gums.

The badger lapped the water at the edge of the brook after eating five nestling rabbits, and the barn owl, continuing its foray, flew along the railway and settled on a signal post from where it listened to two field voles quarrelling in the grass below. Then, as silently as it had landed, it took to the air again and made for Waterlane Farm.

After giving birth to seven kittens, Gytha lay exhausted but contented, her body forming an arc around her sucklings and her legs extended to enclose them. Each had taken its fill of her first flow of milk, which would give it immunity to disease during the early part of its life, and now all seven slept soundly. Gytha too was sated, her stomach full of the seven blood-filled afterbirths, which returned to her body the valuable nutrients she had lost through her pregnancy.

During the early hours, there were other hunters and their prey abroad or lying vigilant over their offspring. Inside Dark Wood, above Oxlease, a doe rabbit suckled her four week-old kittens in a hole she had dug away from the main warren. The blind-ending burrow, or stop, descended several feet into the soft Cotswold sand, and unlike most of the burrows in the warren, it was only wide enough to allow the slimmer-headed doe to enter. The nest chamber was lined with dried grass and moss, and had a thick lining of fur that the doe had plucked from her dewlap. She had given birth at the time of the new moon, when Gytha had just begun to prepare her own nest.

While the doe nursed her kittens, she didn't hear the dog fox padding softly over the ground above her nest and beneath the tree where a tawny owl perched. The owl sat silent and unperturbed, its head rotating in a wide arc to enable its large, lugubrious eyes to follow the fox's movements. During the night, the fox had travelled from Frocester, where a medieval tithe barn stood. In this huge barn, built more than six centuries before by John de Gamages, Abbot of Gloucester, Gytha's ancestors had hunted mice amongst the corn and other tithes from the Benedictine monastery.

The fox had followed a brook course to its spring source at the foot of the limestone escarpment, where Stone Age hunter-gatherers and farmers once collected water in deerskin vessels, and walked along the edge of Pen Wood, where rabbits had burrowed since their escape from medieval warrens. He climbed the steep, grassy slopes to the summit of Selsley Common, cratered by old stone workings, and after crossing the ancient ridgeway road, which formed Woodchester's western boundary, he scaled the drystone wall surrounding Dark Wood. He had paired up with a vixen the previous December, and had courted her on the grassy ramparts of the Iron Age hill fort of Uley, which overlooked the vale and beyond to the Forest of Dean. The pair hunted together throughout the winter, until the leaves of celandines broke through the frosty soil. One night the vixen was caught in a snare, and, the following night, the dog fox, bereft of his mate, stepped into the iron-toothed jaws of a gin trap. Though held fast by one broken, black-socked forepaw, he managed to escape by gnawing through skin, sinew and splintered bone. Since that time the wound had healed leaving a hairless, horny stump.

After exploring Dark Wood, he left by crawling under a wooden five-bar gate into Oxlease, where he surprised a hedgehog foraging for beetles among the dried cowpats. Awakened by the mild April nights, the hedgehog had not long since abandoned its winter nest beneath the roots of an old beech stump. The fox flipped the hedgepig over on to its back with one deft flick of his sound forepaw, and with several snaps of his slim but powerful jaws bit into its throat before it could roll into a ball. Despite his handicap, the wily animal pinned down the twitching urchin with his maimed paw and ripped open the spineless belly with his long canines. Hungry after his night's trek, he feasted on the succulent flesh until only the spiny skin remained.

The hedgehog's mate heard her partner's squeals and took refuge beneath some brambles. Sometime after the fox had limped off, the sow hedgehog ventured out, hesitant and wary. Snuffling and grunting, she foraged for beetle grubs among the grass roots. Soon she came upon the spiny remnants of her mate scattered over the grass, and the lingering smell of fox made her turn in her tracks and run for cover.

Above the edge of the wold the indigo sky paled to aquamarine, extinguishing all the stars and planets. The tawny owl, its eyes closed and mandibles open wide, disgorged a pellet of compacted fur and bone, which bounced off a beech bough and landed among the wood anemones and dog's mercury covering the floor of the wood. A chorus of robin, wren and dunnock, blackbird and thrush sounded from the hedgerows and woodland edge. The solitary badger snored in his sandy set, and the barn owl dozed beneath the rafters at Waterlane Farm. In the dim light of dawn a sharp-eyed robin sifted through the leaf litter beneath the hedgerow along Watery Lane. The redbreast could discern every minute movement for some distance along the hedge bottom, where thrush and blackbird also foraged. The hedgerow was not yet in full leaf, and amongst the field maple the nest of a song thrush was just visible. The hen bird sat on her five black-speckled, turquoise-blue eggs, her body perfectly still, except for a barely discernible ruffling of her crown feathers by the breeze that blew through the laid hedge.

While the hazel's spent catkins shrivelled and leaf buds burst, the thrush had toiled at her nest-building for almost a week. She had made countless journeys, with her beak full of dried grass and fine roots, all collected along the hedgerow. She made the nest platform secure with sticky clay loam, dug from hoof imprints made by cows around the red-brick barn, which stood at the north-eastern corner of Oxlease. From the same barn she gathered dried dung, which she mixed with saliva to make an insulating lining for the tightly woven nest cup.

The thrush's mate hopped along the hedge bottom in search of the elusive grove snail that hid among the leaf litter. He picked up one of the banded snails and flew with it into the lane, where he had taken others that morning. Scattered over the tarmac lay fragments of brown-banded yellow and pink shells he had broken to extract the succulent snails. Holding it by the brown lip, he repeatedly smashed the snail's shell against the tarmac and picked off the broken pieces, like someone peeling a hard-boiled egg,

15

so that he could pull out and eat the soft parts. Then he wiped his beak clean of the snail's glutinous secretions by rubbing it against a fallen elm branch. Before returning to the hedge bottom to seek out more of the camouflaged shells, he sipped the spring water that ran down the steep side of the lane from the stone trough set in the bank.

For many years the old water trough had been a drinking place for farm horse and human alike. Even during the driest of summers it was never empty and always provided a welcome sight to the weary walker. Some local people found that the water was even a cure for certain eye complaints. The trough had been hewn from a block of Old Red Sandstone, though it was not known whether it had been quarried from the banks of the Avon or in the Forest of Dean. The sandstone had been chosen for its peculiar endurance to water, being superior to the local limestone. No one could say how old the trough was or when it was set in the bank, or whether its water had been used to quench the thirst of woolpack horses and drovers treading this ancient road between Bath and Gloucester.

The trough was constantly replenished with water pouring from an iron pipe embedded in the bank at the spot where an underground spring flowed. The water was cool and crystal clear, and where the mason had cut a notch in the rim, it overflowed into a gutter, down which it trickled in an incessant stream. Over the sides of the trough the wet sandstone nourished lowly liverworts and mosses. On the bottom of the trough lay a thick sediment of fine sand and clay mixed with tiny pieces of limestone, which the subterranean stream carried with it when in full spate.

Rain that fell on the limestone common of Selsley, above Dark Wood, found its way through fissures in the rock, filling them as water floods an old mineworking. This natural underground reservoir incessantly percolated the yellow Cotswold sand and flowed along an underlying bed of impervious clay to burst out of the hillside as springs. The Roman engineers who constructed the water supply for the villa of Woodchester knew the whereabouts of these same springs, and led the water through underground stone aqueducts and leaden pipes to feed their baths and cisterns.

The shrill, cascading song of a cock willow warbler perching at the top of a hazel was of too high a register to be heard by the farm labourer on his way down the lane to work. The melodious migrant had arrived in the valley the previous night, after his marathon flight from the African continent. The delicate beauty of his diminutive body was equalled only by the splendour of his singing. His plumage displayed colours that were only to be found in the buds and young leaves of the hedgerows. The warbler had flown into the parish with other cock birds, each of whom sought out a song post on a parcel of land from which he could advertise himself to the hen birds that would shortly arrive.

Above the warbler's song the piercing alarm note of a cock blackbird rang out, and was quickly followed by that of robin and wren. The blackbird flew out of the hedge into Oxlease, his tail jerking and amber bill uttering cries of consternation at the sight of the small predator lurking in the hedge bank. A female, or doe, weasel, unnerved by the cacophony, ran along the bank, weaving a path between the ancient hazel stocks. Dotted along the steep bank on the eastern side of the lane, beneath the hazel roots, were holes of bank voles and wood mice, into which the energetic hunter would momentarily vanish, only to reappear at another spot further along the lane, her white chest grimy from her underground explorations.

Still scolding, though with less fervour, the blackbird flew back into the hedge, and a jenny wren resumed her foray for tiny insects and spiders. As the animated, sinuous form moved in the direction of the water trough, the robin grew more agitated and made brief, frantic flights from one hazel branch to another in pursuit of the short-legged mouser. A few yards away, on her nest in the opposite ivy-covered bank, a hen robin heard the gibing cries of her mate, and she sat tightly on her clutch of six eggs. The weasel stopped suddenly in her tracks, and making a rapid about-turn she sat bolt upright, with her tail held out against the ground to steady herself, and peered up at the defiant cock robin.

The doe weasel was even smaller than the bitch stoat Gytha. Her body was petite and wiry, and her shorter, thinner tail lacked the royal hunter's black tag. Her slender, supple spine supported an inquisitive, mouse-like head that enabled her to squeeze through the narrowest of mouse and vole holes, and which concealed a pair of small but most deadly jaws armed with needle-sharp teeth. Two small dewberry-dark eyes gleamed from the glossy nut-brown fur of her head and back. On the underside of her body the fur was pure white and made a ragged contour where it joined the brown. There was a small brown spot on either side of her white throat, and two larger, irregular patches along the middle of her trim belly. So variable were these markings that in no two animals, even from the same litter, were they identical, and therefore individuals could be told apart by naturalists who studied these elusive hunters.

The weasel had spent most of the past harsh winter living in the neighbourhood of Waterlane Farm, sleeping in corn ricks and haystacks, and hunting mice and rats that lived and multiplied in them. Some of her littermates had also taken up residence around the farm during the winter months. One of her three sisters had been caught by the barn owl and another killed by a farm cat.

Several weeks had passed since the doe had mated with a buck weasel, which roamed from another farm more than two miles away beyond the valley of the Frome. She now carried six young in her belly, and had left the farm to hunt along drystone walls and hedgerows, where she terrorised mice and voles in their burrows and runs and slept off her meals in their nests.

Ignoring the chiding robin, the weasel dropped on to all fours and disappeared into a patch of pungent-smelling hedge garlic, passing close to the robin's nest concealed in the bank. The cock robin, still uttering subdued cries, flew from branch to branch, until the weasel had passed out of sight. Just below the water trough, another robin spotted the villain of the hedgerow as she darted across the lane, her pliant body undulating and her underparts flashing white.

Soon after cowman George Fawkes had fetched in his herd from Oxlease, the sun came up over Rodborough Common. Gytha stood over her young, licked them, and lay down again to suckle them. As they sucked on her full teats, she held one forepaw above her reclined head and groomed the silky cream fur on the inside of her arm. Her coat was now even more sleek and less dense, for the thicker one she had worn through the past winter had almost moulted. After the young stoats had taken their fill, she stood up, taking care not to tread on them. Already she had begun to recover some of her former vitality, and despite her strong bonding to her newborn, she responded to a longing for the world beyond the dark den.

She scaled the vertical wall of the tree hole and looked warily from the entrance, which was only slightly wider than her slim head. Her descent of the alder was unnoticed by a woodpigeon basking in a nearby larch, and it never wavered from its crooning call. She bounded into the field next to the millpond and rubbed her belly through the dewy grass, propelling herself along with her hindlegs, while holding her forelegs against her sides. Then she rolled over on to her back and rubbed it vigorously against the compressed stems, twisting and turning her supple body and lashing her tail. Next she ran her flanks over the grass until it was beaten down by her morning toilet. The feel of the cool dew braced her stiff muscles and the sun's rays penetrated her wet pelt, giving her renewed energy. She lay down in the sun and groomed, then began licking up the beads of dew that hung from the grass blades she had not flattened. Her beautiful coat was cleansed of the stale nest odours and those of her own secretions, so that she felt invigorated and alert to all the sights and sounds around her. She was ready to hunt.

She prowled through the grass even more quietly than a cat,

stopping frequently to investigate the runs of field voles, for it was in the nature of the smaller bitch stoat to favour the flesh of the meadow mouse, as it was once known, which abounded wherever the grass grew rank and ungrazed. But despite her desire for food, she knew that she should not leave her young for too long. Soon she fell upon the scent of a field vole. It sat in its grassy form, half-shaded from the sun, devouring the succulent grass stems. The insatiable rodent took regular lengths of freshly cut stem in its tiny agile paws, guiding each in turn through its sensitive pink lips and slicing off neat, juicy chunks between its razor-edged incisor teeth. The vole was most particular about its food, for it was inclined to eat only the sweet and sappy part of the stalk, and the drier portion it threw away. In a short space of time the ground around its feet was littered with these discarded cuttings.

Gytha crept stealthily along the corridor of grass stems, which was the voles' highway above ground. As the hungry animals moved through the stems, biting them off close to the ground, they created a maze wide enough for the slim bitch stoat to hunt along. The vole stopped eating. It licked the pads of its forepaws and rubbed them briskly over its russet-tinged, grey face and small ears, repeating the action several times, and then paused to listen before cutting another stalk. Gytha heard the sound of the vole's teeth chomping on the grass, and she lowered her head and body still closer to the ground.

Through an opening in the grass she watched the vole, and she cowered even lower, her black tail tassel twitching in anticipation. When only a few body lengths from her preoccupied prey, she sprang, her claws outstretched, ready to strike. Her jaws closed on the vole's back, her canines piercing the backbone and severing the vital spinal cord. She examined her kill, sniffing it and licking up the blood that flowed from the tiny wounds. She placed one paw lightly on the vole's limp body, looked timorously around, then grasped it by the nape and made off in the direction of her den.

A cock robin noticed the brief scuffle in the grass and gave its alarm as Gytha ran home with her booty. She climbed the alder under cover of the ivy, except for the last few feet, when she grasped the bare bark, holding her prey to one side until she reached the tree hole. Safely inside, she settled down to eat the vole and suckle her kittens once more.

The Old Priory

III

Alongside the brook, in an overgrown osier, a cock willow warbler sang and kept a watchful eye over his mate as she pulled slivers of papery bark from a vine of wild clematis that hung from a gnarled, hundred-year-old hawthorn. The Cotswold creeper, better known when its feathery fruits festoon the hedgerows as old man's beard or traveller's joy, was called blithytwine by some local lads, who smoked its woody stems until they were dizzy and sick. The willow warbler's mate had recently arrived in the valley with other females, some of whom had flown further up the hillside where more males sang their sparkling songs. She flew into an elder tree with streamers of bark trailing from her bill, and the cock bird followed her. He fluttered from branch to branch in close attendance, and at each new perch he tilted his head to show the olive-green plumage of his crown and the thin, pale yellow crescent over his eye. At intervals he gave a plaintive 'hooeet' to his mate, who flew to her nest in the long grass that lay between the brook and the main road to Stroud.

Beneath a tussock, partly hollowed out by field voles and once occupied by a nest of bumblebees, the hen bird worked the blithytwine bark into the grass stems to form a dome over her nest, in the side of which she had left a neat entrance hole. Again she flew out from the grass to collect more bark, and her mate, who had resumed his singing, suddenly became silent and pursued her. Now he began to call out urgently, for he had caught sight of a weasel in the grass, and the hen bird flew higher into the hawthorn tree.

The buck weasel, not yet a yearling, had recently woken from his early morning sleep in a bank vole's nest beneath the drystone wall on the far side of the road. During the night he had travelled almost two miles from woodland further up the valley. Where the remains of last year's beechmast lay against the wall, he had caught a wood mouse as it ventured from its hole in search of a mate. The weasel had been born while the beechnuts were still milky. He wore a dense pelt of a pale chocolate colour, and the pattern of markings on his underside differed in detail from that of each of his six siblings. The young buck had become independent of his mother as the beechnuts ripened, and unlike his half-brothers and -sisters from an earlier litter, born as the beeches came into leaf, he was slow to reach adulthood.

Further down the brook, where the dark water flowed under a stone bridge past an old withy bed, another willow warbler sang from the top of an alder, unaware of the weasel hunting along the bank. A blue tit gave the alarm and hopped agitatedly backwards and forwards along the branch of an oak, raising and lowering its cobalt-blue crown feathers and uttering sharp, scolding cries. From the chimney top of a cottage by the roadside a cock blackbird sang his ebullient song. In a nest built in the cotoneaster that grew against the cottage wall, the blackbird's mate felt her four well-brooded eggs roll against her mottled brown breast. The previous spring the loyal pair of birds had nested in the same spot. Their four nestlings were barely fledged when a cat climbed down from the porch on to the bush and took them from the nest. But a week later the persistent hen was brooding another clutch.

The blackbird at his song post was oblivious of the cries coming from the garden by the side of the brook, where a hen song thrush piped dolefully as she watched the weasel carry off one of her four nestlings. Above the blackbird's song sounded a goods train trundling along the branch line towards the nearby industrial town of Stroud. Couplings clanked as the wagons' buffers rebounded against one another behind the braking engine. From its funnel thick white smoke billowed along the embankment, momentarily quietening humming honeybees that worked the yellow catkins of pussy willow and smarting the eyes of two young boys who searched for birds' nests. Some of the bees returned laden with pale yellow pollen to a nearby elm, where their waxen combs filled the hollow trunk. The previous year, a swarm from a hive in the garden where the blackbird sang found the elm, and through the summer built six curtains of comb in the tree's dark cavity.

The oily locomotive let out an explosive jet of hissing steam, which sent rabbits running for their burrows at the top of the embankment. The engine slowed to walking pace, and the driver and fireman leant out of their cab to peer at the grey animal with the black and white head lying at the side of the track. During the night the old badger from the set near Watery Lane had crossed the line and had been hit by the last goods train. Soil and fur still stuck to his long-clawed forepaws, for he had dug out his last nest of baby rabbits from the embankment. In another hole close by a stoat had heard the noisy badger digging through the soil, following his keen nose as he went.

Venting blasts of smoke and steam, the engine picked up speed again and rolled towards Stroud. After the swirling smoke had cleared away, the dog stoat woke from his short sleep in one of the rabbit burrows and climbed out through a scoot-hole, from which he had bolted two rabbits just before sunrise. The stoat was a fine yearling who had migrated from an estate on the far side of the Frome, where he had been born the previous spring. He was hunting on the domain of the dog stoat Aethelwald, who only the day before had slept in a neighbouring rabbit hole. Stretched out on the grass, the royal hunter enjoyed the sunshine. A bumblebee flew past him and settled on a grass blade a few feet away. The queen buff-tailed bumblebee, who had not long emerged from her winter's sleep in an old wood mouse nest, groomed the yellow and tan hairs covering her bulbous, egg-filled abdomen with her hindmost pair of legs.

The stoat sat up and watched, then cautiously stalked over to inspect the bee, who began to crawl clumsily over the grass, pausing now and then to rub her front legs over the back of her head, where tiny mites lodged between the hairs. The inquisitive stoat backed away a few paces as the drowsy humbledore suddenly changed direction, tracing an unsteady path between the grass stems, and all the while letting out a low, languid drone. Then she accelerated from her listless ramblings and took to the air, startling the bemused stoat as she flew close to him on wings that seemed ill-designed to carry her cumbersome-looking body. Before she had flown a rail's length along the embankment, she alighted amongst a clump of white deadnettle flowers, which in the sun's warm rays emitted a faint scent from the sugary nectar at the bottom of their deep throats. Making ungainly flights to selected flowers, she probed the tubular petals and drew up the energy-giving liquor through her long, flexible tongue. Then after a short whirling flight she rose into the sky and made for her nest in an old wood mouse burrow, beneath a hawthorn hedge bordering one of the small meadows over which the barn owl hunted.

A doe rabbit stopped grooming and sat upright with ears pricked to watch the stoat bounding over the embankment. Following a well-worn path used by generations of badgers to reach their watering place at the edge of the brook, the stoat disturbed a blackbird foraging for her young beneath some brambles. The hen bird fled in a frenzy into a hawthorn bush, her beak crammed with severed lengths of earthworm. Having eaten his fill of rabbit, the stoat showed no interest in the birds that foraged in the undergrowth. The boys whose pockets held the eggs of song thrush, dunnock and wren, glimpsed the elusive hunter as he crossed the path at the bottom of the embankment some way ahead of them. As he turned to look in their direction, they noticed the white front and the black-tipped tail, and they recognised the creature they had seen last summer gambolling among the rabbits on one of Woodchester's warrens.

The stoat darted into the spinney through which the old millstream flowed, and not even the rustling of dried leaves could be heard as the fleet-footed hunter moved over the woodland floor. Passing the spot where they had seen the stoat cross the footpath, the young naturalists smelled a musky odour they knew belonged to a fox that had also recently gone that way.

In the spinney, a grey squirrel that was feeding high up in a beech tree, spotted the stoat and froze where it squatted, grasping a bunch of young catkins between its paws. With the coming of spring the rodent's silver-grey coat had become more sleek and was washed with a bright rufous colour over its feet and flanks, so that it had sometimes even been mistaken for the native red squirrel.

Unlike its close cousin with the russet pelt, the rat-like squirrel was a relative newcomer to the wold. It was descended from animals brought from the New World by men who were more fascinated by exotic animals than the elusive native ones of their own country. The squirrels were kept in menageries and on country estates, and were even released into the countryside. In a few decades they had populated the country far and wide. The alert squirrel crouched on the beech branch, eyeing the stoat as he scented around the base of the tree. When it could no longer see his lively movements through the leafing branches, the squirrel climbed further along the bough to reach more of the tree's succulent flowers.

The stoat left the spinney and made for the drystone wall that surrounded the mansion known as the Old Priory. He stopped to sniff at one of the coping stones that had fallen from the top of the wall and smelled the scent of another stoat. Further along he came to a gap in the wall where a larch tree had blown down in a gale. The stones lay in a pile waiting for a waller to make good the damage to the mortarless masterpiece. He climbed over the stones and leaped into the well-kept garden.

The mansion, more than three centuries old, had been built over the foundations of the original manor house of Woodchester, and stood close to the site of the great Roman villa. The house once obtained its water from the same springs that supplied the villa, and which the Romans led through limestone and leaden pipes. The owners called it 'Vespasian Water'. The first mansion was built in Norman times by the Maltravers family from the stones of the villa, and the land that surrounded it and the Norman church was the first Woodchester Park. Lord of the manor, Baron Maltravers, was one of the keepers of King Edward II, and was said to have had a part in his brutal murder at Berkeley Castle. The Huntley family, who were granted the manor of Woodchester by Elizabeth I, also lived there, until Sir George Huntley built a Tudor mansion in a wooded valley in South Woodchester, which he enclosed with a drystone wall. This became the Woodchester Park of today.

Over the years the cream-coloured Cotswold stone of the Old Priory's walls and mullions had weathered to a delicate shade of grey, and on the hand-hewn stone roof tiles lichens grew in the clean air, as they had done on the tiles of the villa sixteen centuries before. Through one of the open windows came the sound of children's laughter. As he galloped across the lawn, the stoat stopped and cocked his head at the little girl who came running from the house. The child called to her sister to come and see the beautiful creature in the garden. But she had hardly uttered her cries of delight when the stoat vanished into the shadow of the high stone wall that separated the garden from the old churchyard. Sheltering in one of its many cavities, he rested awhile, listening to the hurried footsteps of the excited children on the gravel drive.

A cock chaffinch, his pink breast feathers glowing in the sun, sang his vigorous song from a lime tree, drowning the feeble calls of goldcrests in a yew. The stoat crept out from his refuge, looked over towards the house to see the child skipping back along the drive, and then ran alongside the wall, searching for a way through into the graveyard belonging to the remains of the old Norman parish church. Among the rough grass that grew against the graveyard wall the stoat prowled like a cat stalking a bird. The chaffinch, seeing the movement in the grass, flew to a higher branch, flashing his white tail feathers, and gave his metallic 'chwink, chwink' call of alarm.

Hidden from view in a yew tree that overhung the wall, a pair of goldcrests called to one another. Their high-pitched voices could not be heard by the gardener tending the graveyard, and the split-second shimmer of the cock bird's flame-coloured crown was only seen by the hen as she bound her mossy nest to the yew bough with twisted silken threads of spiders' webs. The diminutive cock, even smaller than the jenny wren, fluttered to the ground and pulled at the soft, green moss that grew at the foot of a gravestone. As he flew up into the yew with moss blowing from his bill, the shrewd gardener glanced up and saw the blaze of the orange crest against the dark green needles. While the cock called from the dense foliage, the hen tugged at spiders' webs in the wall's recesses. Back at the nest, the diligent hen attached the silken threads to the delicate, mossy cradle, binding firmly a few more strands of moss that her mate had just delivered. In the breeze the exquisite structure moved in unison with every small movement of the pliant bough from which it was suspended.

The stoat woke from his brief sleep beneath the drystone wall and licked his paws, which an hour earlier had pulled down a fledgling blackbird. With its three nest mates the young bird had taken its first unsteady flight, watched by the stoat under cover of the long grass. At one corner of the graveyard a sprinkling of dusky feathers marked the spot where the bird had met its fate. Leaving the graveyard by a vole run that emerged on the other side of the wall, the stoat detected the scent of a weasel, which regularly hunted voles beneath the stony foundations.

Earlier that morning the weasel had taken a bank vole to its den beneath a tombstone standing at the edge of an expanse of turf devoid of gravestones, under which the great Roman pavement lay buried. The ornately carved memorial of lichen-encrusted freestone bore the name of a local clothier, who two and a half centuries before had grown wealthy from the ancient woollen trade that had its beginnings in the valley. During his short life, like many merchants of his kind, the clothier had been a benefactor to the community among which he lived and worked.

Finding himself back in the garden of the mansion, the stoat followed the high wall under cover of a long herbaceous border. Soon he discovered a hole large enough to squeeze through into the meadow called Shortcombe, where the grass grew lush after the recent rain. Swallows skimmed the field, snapping up flies that had emerged from their winter quarters beneath the decaying vegetation along the hedgerows. Each spring the black flies began to appear so close to St Mark's Eve that men had named them after the saint. Keeping within the cover of the long grass that grew alongside the wall, the stoat ran towards the stream. When almost a quarter of the way along the bank he scented a moorhen, which a short while before had squatted in the grass to preen itself. Several yards ahead, partly hidden by a clump of rush, the bird pecked at the damp vegetation for the slugs and snails that lived there.

Earlier that morning the moorhen, more aptly called the waterhen, and which the Saxons called the merehen, had left the millpond on whose reedy margin she had her nest, for the lame dog fox had taken every one of her ten unbrooded eggs. The stoat paused where a willow branch had fallen across the stream, and where it threw out new olive-green shoots he again detected the same unfamiliar scent of another stoat. Reaching up to his full height, he peered over the top of the branch, with his forepaws resting lightly on the bark, but all he saw was a swallow swoop low over the grass to take another St Mark's fly.

On the Selsley side of the boundary stream, where new vegetation was beginning to hide the woody stems of last year's willowherb, the moorhen watched the stoat run across the willow branch and canter along the bank towards Watery Lane, and with a flirt of its tail it scuttled off through the willowherb stems towards the millpond. The stoat crossed the lane and slipped under the five-bar gate into Oxlease. Gathered around the red-brick barn cows lay quietly cudding, wisps of steam rising from their warm backs, wet from the last shower.

A Gloucester with a crooked horn peered at the royal hunter as he began to perform his strange antics. As though with intent to entertain, he ran about the field in front of the ruminating beast, twisting and turning and springing over the grass with the boundless energy characteristic of his race. The cow was bemused, her head describing short arcs as she followed the stoat's dance. Then the stoat bounded up to a Friesian, whose mouth was rimmed with saliva, green-tinged from the sappy grass she regurgitated. When barely a foot away, he stood on his hindlegs and gazed up at the black and white cow, sniffing the warm, strangely scented breath blowing from the huge, flared nostrils.

Next a blue roan shorthorn got up and ambled over to watch the sporting stoat, and soon other cows came to investigate. The stoat stood more erect, balancing himself on the base of his tail. Like a cobra eyeing its prey, he moved his head slowly from side to side, and, as suddenly as an autumn leaf is carried by a gust of wind, he turned a somersault and dashed into the hedge. Unknowingly he passed close to the nest of a willow warbler hidden in the grass and safeguarded from the browsing cows by a thorny-stemmed dog rose brier. The pair of warblers called out to one another in an alder, from whose branches the new season's green cones hung alongside last year's woody ones, picked clean by winter flocks of redpolls, tits and siskins.

The stoat explored a blackthorn thicket that stood at the corner of Oxlease. He watched a swallow collecting clay from the edge of the spring-fed stream in the neighbouring meadow, which was known by some as 'claypits', for it had once been a local source of brick clay. Travelling the same route as the willow warbler, the swallow had arrived a week ago. As it dug and scraped, the timid bird constantly looked around, but before the stoat could put one foot forward, it took flight, its tail streamers lightly brushing the rushes as it ascended. It flew down the meadow, skimmed over the hedge into Oxlease, and darted through a hole in the hayloft door of the barn. The foundations of its nest were cemented to a rafter, and only a foot away from that which its parents had built the previous year. With its innate skill the swallow emptied its bill of mud, which it pressed into the still moist pellets collected a short while before. Among the rafters past generations of swallows had built their nests, each fashioned from mud out of the same stream and straws gleaned from around the barn.

The stoat made his way to the top of a meadow where huge heaps of yellow Cotswold sand, excavated and trodden bare by badgers, showed up amid the stinging nettles and elder trees. He climbed a steep bank, criss-crossed by badger paths and surmounted by a line of ash trees. The mounds of compacted soil were piled around the bases of the trees, some of whose bark was scored by badgers' claws. No one knew how long badgers had lived there. One wise old man had been told by his father's father that they had always lived in nearby Dark Wood. How far their burrows penetrated the hillside was also a mystery. But the same countryman reckoned that, from the vast amount of earth the indomitable diggers had shifted during his lifetime, there must be a real honeycomb of workings beneath the field and wood.

Like its distant cousin the stoat, the badger had a most ancient lineage stretching back to the time of the great Ice Age. When the first human hunters came to the wold they found the wooded combes abounding in badgers, and they knew from the land of their birth that the pig-like animals were good to eat, for they had dug them out from their burrows and baited them with dogs. Although through the centuries the harmless creatures had been hunted and persecuted by man and their woodland home threatened, they had survived to frequent every hanger and many a hedge bank in the parish.

At the top of the bank the stoat stopped to smell the bleached skull of a rabbit, which a badger had unearthed when it had enlarged its set. The skull bore the strong scent left by the dog stoat Aethelwald, and the yearling sensed he was on the domain of another. He sat up on his haunches, looked about, and scented the breeze that rustled the ivy covering one of the ash trees. Across the meadow he saw a magpie intent on sucking a song thrush's egg it had filched from Dark Wood. The ivy leaves rustled a little louder, and the yearling turned his head towards the sound. Around the crown of the tree, where the evergreen creeper grew thickest, the ivy leaves shook as Aethelwald scrambled down. When several feet from the ground, he jumped on to one of the badger spoil heaps and stood with his back arched and his fine brush waving. He had been resting in the tree and had been watching the yearling as he came up the bank. Making a kind of cackling noise, Aethelwald bounded towards the intruder, who cowered with ears flattened and tail tip flicking.

Aethelwald ran a half-circle round the yearling and drew himself up on his hindlegs, chattering through bared teeth. The yearling flinched at the dominant dog's threat calls, but stood his ground, the hairs on his neck and back bristling and his brush brandishing the air. As Aethelwald approached the yearling, the magpie, which had been watching from one of the ash trees, flew down to the ground. Aethelwald stopped in his tracks, as though distracted by the colourful crow, and the yearling, gaining in courage, edged nearer to his adversary.

The inquisitive magpie hopped over the grass towards the stoats, giving its familiar 'chatchatchatchack' call. Cackling loudly, Aethelwald made a mock strike at the yearling's flank, at which the submissive animal leapt into the air over the back of his challenger, and went down the meadow at full gallop. For several moments Aethelwald looked in the direction the yearling had gone. Then he sat down and smoothed out the ruffled hairs around his rump, turned to see the magpie fly off, and bounded towards Dark Wood.

Wrought iron gate into Oxlease

IV

The sun came up over Rodborough Common, casting long shadows of the ashes and beeches that fringed its grassy slopes, and reflecting like flames in the windows of houses on the opposite hillside. The large, mullioned windows of old weavers' cottages of Atcombe Terrace in South Woodchester mirrored the sun's rays as they had done in centuries past, when home looms rattled and clacked in the light and airy workrooms. The cottages stood alongside the old road that led to North Woodchester, where at the village bakehouse, halfway up steep Selsley Road, Ernest Garraway removed crusty bread and lardie cake from the coke-fired ovens. In the backyard of a neighbouring terraced house old Mrs Driver pumped water into a pail to fill her copper for the morning wash. From an old drystone pound adjoining a house called Larchgrove Cottage, a rooster's strident call resounded around the hillside.

Cowman George Fawkes walked along Watery Lane to fetch in his herd for the morning milking. Behind the high stone wall that enclosed the grounds of a big house called the Lawn, the expanding palm-like leaves of horse chestnut trees were already casting their shade over the lane. By the stone barn where a screech owl sometimes roosted, George opened the ornate wrought iron gate into Oxlease and called to his charges. His regular appearance at the top of the field at the same time each morning and afternoon was often sufficient to attract the attention of several cows, and now it was a blue roan shorthorn and red Gloucester who alerted others in the herd. Only a few cows were reluctant to follow the rest, and these George encouraged by calling out their names in his rich Gloucestershire brogue. Soon they had all left the field and were jostling for positions along the muck-strewn lane.

At the end of the lane the colourful herd, tails swinging and distended udders swaying, descended the hill that led to Fawkes' farm. The red Gloucester with the crooked horn lingered over a patch of lush grass at the edge of the road, and after a few gentle prods of George's hazel stick she followed on the heels of the others. Each cow, who was named after a wayside or woodland flower, had a personality of her own, and to the cowman was much more than a milk-yielding commodity. A dun shorthorn halted to gaze inquisitively through long eyelashes at a cat standing with arched back on the bakehouse wall, and a Friesian found satisfaction from rubbing her rump against the wall of the Lawn. At the bend in the road, opposite the rectory gates, the herd entered the farmyard.

The lowing of cows and clanking of pails came from the milking parlour where the Fawkes' brothers hand-milked the herd. Warm frothy milk was poured into the cooler, where it ran over corrugated stainless steel to be collected in dented, well-worn churns. Then one by one the cows were released from their stalls into the farmyard, where they stood close together waiting to be taken back to Oxlease. A pied wagtail walked briskly among them, picking up insects to take to his mate who was brooding her eggs in a nest built amongst a stack of old bean sticks in the farm garden.

The farm cat sat dozing in the sun on a warm flagstone outside the farmhouse door. Before sunrise it had caught a young blackbird and had left some of its feathers beneath a laurel in the next-door garden. Like the royal hunter the cat was a fine exponent of stealth. At this time of year it would wander along the hedgerows and drystone walls at night and in the early morning in search of furred and feathered prey. Often in summer it would lie in wait on some grassy bank or wall, or lurk in the tall grass of a hay meadow ready to ambush a passing weasel. Even stoats had succumbed to its clawing grasp and the deft strike of its jaws. Not for want of food did the fatal felid prey on these small members of the weasel tribe, but because its instinct to stalk and spring at moving prey was rooted in a lineage as long as that of the royal hunter.

The church clock struck the half-hour as George Fawkes took his cows back to Oxlease. Closing the gate behind them, he heard the anxious rattle of a cock wren whose mate had her nest in the stone barn. He knew the wren's cries signalled the nearness of a four-footed predator, and he looked over the wall of the Lawn in the direction of the sounds. But even his keen eye could discern no movement among the thickets of snowberry that grew between the horse chestnut trees. The jenny wren sitting on her clutch of seven eggs heard her mate marking the movement of a weasel through the thickets. Other sounds too only the brooding bird heard, for from within her eggs came the cheeping of her young. Small blisters had begun to appear on the shells where the convulsing chicks hammered with their toothed bills to release themselves.

In the hedge bottom along Watery Lane the cuckoo pint displayed its peculiar blooms. The pale green, cowl-like spathes exposed their pink or purple pokers. Over the centuries the sight of this familiar flower evoked in country folk such names as wake robin, cows and calves, and wild arum. Some had dubbed the plant cuckoo pint because its curious poker appeared around the time the first cuckoo was heard. Others called it lords and ladies, because those plants with pink pokers were reminiscent of the fairer sex, and those with purple ones of masculinity. It was the appearance of this strange maturing flower that had even given rise to the name Jack-in-the-pulpit. A few plants growing at the sunlit edge of the hedge bottom had flowers that were in their prime. In one the spathe had fully parted to reveal the base of the poker, or spadix, encircled by its colourless, nondescript flowerlets.

A multitude of midges flitted through the hedge bottom, lured by the carrion-like odour given off by each ripe, stinking spadix. The flies had hatched from cowpat puddles and hoof imprints in Oxlease, and it was their nature to be attracted to such foetid smells. Some of the minute, moth-like insects settled on the colourful pokers and began to seek out the rotten flesh that the deceitful plants advertised. Other flies that had fallen into the plants' traps the previous evening now crawled out, their downy wings dusted with pollen. These flew to other plants, once more enticed by their rank smell, and falling into the same traps, completed the role Nature had assigned to them. By such deception the cuckoo pint ensured a crop of fertile fruits and therefore its own survival.

In her tree den Gytha encircled her seven kittens. Each was now the size of a field vole and was covered with short, silky fur, similar in colour to the gills of a near-ripe mushroom. On the crown and nape the hair was longer and darker, forming a distinct mane. The kittens lay huddled together in a heap, for in this way, when Gytha was away from them, they kept themselves warm. Also, in such intimate contact they licked up each other's excrement and so helped to keep the nest clean. But it was Gytha who ensured they did not foul the nest by her regular attention to their hindquarters.

Their blunt-nosed, round faces, with eyelids still closed, nuzzled Gytha's warm, milk-laden teats, for it was time for their next meal. Gytha lay on her side to enable them to feed. As she let down her milk she dozed contentedly, with eyes half closed. One of the males sucked greedily on his favourite teat, midway along her belly. As he drew in the rich milk, the lusty young dog lightly pawed at the head of one of his brothers who fed alongside. His chin was wet with the milk that bubbled between his lips. He relaxed his hold on the nipple for a moment and yawned to show the sharp, dull white milk teeth, which during the last few days had cut through the gums.

Already Gytha had begun to wean her kittens by regurgitating from her highly muscular stomach small pieces of field vole, wood mouse, nestling rabbit and fledgling bird. She rolled on to her back to make it easier for some of the kittens to suckle. Some found the teats they fed from yielded less milk than their healthy appetites demanded, while others slid from her belly sated and sleepy. Although in the darkness of the tree hole she could barely see her kittens, she was able to recognise each one, not only by its individual smell, taste and the sounds it made, but by means of the highly tactile vibrissae projecting from her muzzle she was able to judge its form. The firstborn was the liveliest dog, slightly smaller than his three brothers. The lastborn kitten, a bitch, was also larger and more active than her two sisters. Ever since the kittens had uttered their first thin, piercing peeps, these two had always been the most vigorous and vocal of the litter.

For a while after the kittens had taken their fill of her milk, Gytha lay with them, licking each in turn to clean it of its last discharge of excreta. Then she groomed herself, pausing now and then to gaze up at the pale shaft of light that shone through the entrance to the tree hole. Sensing her young were sleeping soundly, she stood up over them, stretched herself as best she could in the confined space, and left them again to hunt. As they felt the touch of her warm body leave them, the kittens huddled closer together, using their limbs and peculiar bending movements of their highly flexible bodies.

The trees in the spinney by the millpond were alive with the songs of thrush, wren and ringdove. A robin, or ruddock, which was the name the Saxons gave the red-breasted bird, saw Gytha crouch down on the ground at the bottom of the alder. Each morning she left her young she would deposit her droppings, or scats, round about the tree, for since she had given birth she had taken care not to foul the nest. The robin also watched her drink at her usual spot at the edge of the millstream. As she ran across the drive which led to the rear of the Old Priory, a cock wren spotted her and delivered his loud clicking call of alarm from his low perch in an elder.

The bobbing bird seemed to taunt the stoat with his vehement cries. But Gytha was accustomed to such a reception, and pausing to cast a disdainful glance at the impetuous bird, she ran into a hedgerow. She pursued a path along the hedge bank where the bare, moist earth held the occasional scent of voles. Some yards ahead, a male bank vole sat boldly grooming his fur in the sun, a few tail-lengths from his hole. His mate was suckling her four naked young in a nest beneath the roots of a crab apple tree. Now and then he interrupted his toilet, his body motionless, except for an occasional quiver of his brown whiskers.

Gytha squeezed her head through the entrance to the bank vole's nursery. She waved her tail excitedly from side to side over the ground as she inhaled the odours that eddied along the dark underground run. Quickly she withdrew her head and scratched vigorously at the soil around the entrance. She stamped her hindfeet and again tried to push her wiry body further into the burrow, but roots and pieces of limestone hindered her progress. Several feet along the tunnel, in a moss-lined nest, the female vole lay closely over her young ones. She and her blind babies were safe for the moment. Her mate, who had been nibbling the young leaves of hawthorn, had winded the royal hunter and scurried back to his own underground refuge.

Tiring of her efforts, Gytha brushed away with her forepaws the soil that had fallen around her ears and stuck to her muzzle. With one muddy paw flexed an inch off the ground, she stood still and peered along the hedge bank, only her head moving in slow, snake-like fashion. She hunted the length of the hedgerow without managing to capture any prey. She slipped beneath a gate and paused for a moment, her tail tag lightly brushing the base of the gatepost, then sped across a footpath and under a stile, which was situated at the corner of another meadow in neighbouring Selsley. She stopped again and looked about her, with arched back supported on hindfeet and balancing tail thrown out behind in a similar flowing curve.

Ahead of her, at the edge of the meadow, just within the limit of her discernible vision, she watched a pair of magpies standing over the remains of a rabbit that a badger had skinned and eaten during the early hours of the morning. The couple pecked at the meagre flesh adhering to the torn, furry skin, and as they feasted they carried on an incessant chatter, which had earned the garrulous bird the Gloucestershire name of maggotty pie. The pied crows noticed the stoat standing watching them at the edge of the field, and both flew, chackering, in single file, to a tall hawthorn where they had their nest. The bulky, twiggy nest was built in the topmost branches, and was surmounted by a dome of thorny sticks to protect the birds' eggs and young from the depredations of its larger cousin, the carrion crow.

The magpie shared with the carrion crow a reputation for stealing the eggs and nestlings of songbirds and ground-nesters. It held a long-standing distrust of man, because for years those who keepered some of the estates outside Woodchester shot and trapped the bird. Many of the magpie's forebears had shared keepers' gibbets with carrion crows, jays and other so-called vermin. Since the passing of the two world wars some keepers never returned to carry on their craft, and so the pied predator was given a respite. In Woodchester the magpie was not persecuted and was accepted among the farming community, for perched on the backs of sheep it helped rid them of insect parasites. However, a few superstitious folk would have preferred not to see the magpie around since they sometimes considered it a portent of death.

The magpies watched Gytha working the hedgerow, her muzzle close on the trail of a doe rabbit who had just left her burrow.

She hesitated by the blocked entrance to a stop. The doe who had dug this, her first nesting burrow, was a last season's animal who had been born during the summer to a queen doe in a warren along the railway embankment. At the approach of winter, the doe wandered off with two of her sisters to seek new ground, and finding an old deserted burrow in a smaller warren, they cleaned it out and enlarged it for themselves. During the winter and early spring the does shared the burrow with a young buck who had roamed from the warren in Dark Wood. A short time after Gytha gave birth, one of the does left her sisters and wandered still farther to prepare a place for her confinement.

The young mother had recently left her week-old kittens to graze in the company of other nursing does. On emerging from her stop, she had been lured by the sight of the other rabbits and the smell of the lush grass that the clay loam supported. But her first instinct had been to plug the stop with dried grass, and with the entrance behind her and a heap of excavated soil in front, she had scraped some of it into the entrance and tamped it down with her forepaws, repeating the process until nearly all the soil was gone. Then with the last heap, she spread wide her back legs and scattered soil between them over the beaten ground, so covering her traces. In this way her young were offered some protection against predators such as stoats, weasels and rats, and even predatory buck rabbits.

Gytha smelled around the concealed stop entrance, but finding no scent there she moved on, diligently searching every hole she encountered. Soon she came upon another stop whose entrance was not blocked. She peered in and crawled cautiously down the short burrow a distance equal to four lengths of her body. The air inside smelled strongly of rabbit. A doe, who the previous night had given birth to six young, growled from the nest chamber at the end of the tunnel. On hearing the threatening sounds, Gytha lost no time retreating from the stop. She remembered the time last summer when, as a newcomer to the warren at the edge of Dark Wood, a nursing doe suddenly appeared at the entrance to its nest and thrust out at her with its powerful hindfeet, hurling her into the air in a spray of soil. The stoat's long memory told her that does defending their young were best avoided.

She began to explore the rough grassland that sloped down to the stream running along the northern end of Shortcombe meadow. The territory over which she hunted was much smaller than that held by Aethelwald. Like the dog stoat, she had her own favourite hedgerows, banks, drystone walls and warrens. These had become familiar to her since she and her brothers and sisters had discovered them during their first summer. When the time had finally come for her to relinquish her family ties, the mated bitch had taken up residence in the same area where she had been born. One of her sisters also had her domain close by, and it too was encompassed by that of Aethelwald.

She cantered through the grass at the field edge. A robin scolded from the hedgerow bordering Watery Lane. A Persian cat prowling through the grass lifted its head to wind the stoat, and continued its quest for early morning, sun-seeking voles. She halted suddenly in her tracks, balancing herself on the toes of her hindfeet, and turning her head over her shoulder she glanced back along the route she had come to see Aethelwald appear from the hedge, his individual scent wafting over the grass to her poised nostrils. He bounded hesitantly towards her, pausing now and then to smell the ground over which she had run. She was used to encountering him at such a distance and gave one of her threatening cackles, at which he disappeared into the hedge.

In the shelter of a hollow hazel stock she ate a vole she had caught in its grassy labyrinth. After quenching her thirst in the stream, she followed its course back to the millpond. A male brimstone butterfly flashed its sulphur-yellow wings as it flew over the marshy ground alongside the stream, in pursuit of a cream-winged female who sought the alder buckthorn on whose leaves it would lay its eggs. Gytha hesitated before she began to climb the ivy-clad alder, for she smelled the scent of Aethelwald, who had rubbed his hindquarters on a fallen branch while she had been away hunting. He had been on one of his patrols at the edge of his domain and had stopped to leave his scent mark.

Gytha had been away from her young for only as long as it had taken Jim Hammond, the milkman from Fawkes' farm, to deliver milk to twelve households up Selsley Road. He lifted one of the small churns from the horse-drawn cart and carried it through the iron front garden gate of Larchgrove Cottage, which was named after a grove of larch trees standing in the grounds of the adjoining house called Larchgrove. He had no need to rap the polished brass knocker that adorned the green door, and which was cast in the likeness of Dickens' Mr Micawber, for the sound of his footsteps on the gravel path and the ring of his churns at this regular early hour were familiar to the woman who lived in the cottage.

Tall, slightly stooping Lilian Cashmore opened the door, smiling through kindly, blue-grey eyes. She exchanged pleasant words with Jim, words that extended beyond mere greeting, for she always had time to speak to all those she met during the day. Time in this small community was not rationed. She held out a jug for Jim to fill, and he dipped a metal measure into the churn and ladled out a quart of rich, raw milk. A few shillings and pence, which was the week's bill, passed hands, and Jim resumed his uphill round.

As Lilian closed the door, her Persian cat slipped into the cottage and followed her into the cool, dimly lit kitchen that led from the single living room. It rubbed its head and flanks against her legs, with its tail held high, and purred loudly in anticipation of the milk it was to receive. After she had fed her cat, she took the lid off the haybox in which she had cooked potatoes for her chickens. She removed the still warm saucepan she had put there the previous night and carried it outside to the wash house. Here she mashed the potatoes in a bucket and mixed in several handfuls of corn meal to make a feed she knew would encourage her hens to lay well. Then she filled a can from the large rainwater tank that stored the clean run-off from the high pitched roof of

Cotswold stone slates, and carried both food and water down the garden path that ran alongside the old pound. She unfastened the ricketty gate, and noticing the wire was coming away from the bottom, she was reminded that she must repair it again to deter the night-roving badger, which she knew was partial to hens' eggs.

The pound, which butted up to the cottage, had once been used to secure stray cattle or sheep that wandered into the hill from the common until they were claimed by their owners. During the whole of her married life Lilian had kept and reared her own chickens in the pound. Throughout the recent war she had never been short of eggs, and because her hens laid more during the year than she and her husband could use, she preserved some for winter, when they would go off lay, in a pail of water glass that she kept in a corner of her cool walk-in pantry, alongside her home-made wine and ginger beer.

The Rhode Island Red hens pecked lustily at the warm mash. The cockerel whose clarion call bothered no one living in the neighbourhood, strutted over the earth floor of the pound on spurred, scaly feet, hustling his harem and gulping large morsels of mash from the trough. The drystone wall of the pound was draped with thick ivy, and in its crevices grew herb robert, ivy-leaved toadflax and spleenwort fern, and where most of the toppers were missing, succulent stoneworts nestled on the crumbling, weathered stone. Over the surface of the limestone glistening, dried-up slime trails showed where moisture-loving snails had travelled during the night to raid the garden. Now they rested, hidden in the wall's dark crannies, digesting the greenstuff they had devoured.

Rising steeply from the cottage and its pound the well-stocked garden was bathed in bright sunlight, for it lay on the east-facing side of Selsley Hill. Besides providing vegetables and fruit, it was a source of pride and contentment to Lilian, and the herbaceous borders that she so carefully tended would, through the seasons, bring a whole range of colour to her homestead. In one corner at the top of the garden stood a brick privy, and next to it a wood and corrugated iron fuel store, where a few beech logs lay on the slacky ground alongside several large lumps of coal. In the opposite top corner there was a garden shed containing crock flower pots, seed trays and garden tools. It also housed Lilian's two pre-war, large-framed Rudge and Humber bicycles on which she rode to Stroud on shopping days, and which she used to get about the parish and more distant places in the hilly hundred. An ivied limestone wall along one side of the garden, and a paling fence at the top, separated the garden from the grounds of the old house, Larchgrove, where Lilian's husband, Ernest, worked as gardener.

Ernie Cashmore trod heavily along the drive, his hobnailed boots scraping the gravel. He opened the door to the apple store and old coach house where the garden tools were kept, and where some of last year's harvest lay in orderly rows on wooden racks. As he was about to close it, a robin flew past his head. The hen had built her nest on the ledge of one of the small windows, and was using a hole in a broken pane to gain entry. Since before sunrise she and her mate had made many visits to their nestlings, flying from all parts of the garden with tiny green caterpillars they caught in the trees. As Ernie watched one of the birds return with food, he noticed again the misshapen tail feathers he had seen on the robin that had followed closely his digging of the previous autumn. The cock robin owed his damaged tail to a surprise encounter with one of a family of weasels that had been reared in the garden during the summer. The young weasel had sprung at the robin as he settled to roost one evening and had broken his tail feathers, but he had escaped to pair a second winter.

The ruddock was a particular ally of the gardener, for along with titmice and other songbirds, particularly in the nesting season, it fed on the insect pests that damaged his crops. Some birds he did not favour, like the bullfinch, which took the young buds from the apple and pear cordons. But although he knew where a pair were starting to build, he would not molest them. A few, like the magpie and jay, he tried to outwit by means of nets, coloured streamers and clanking cans set around the vegetable garden, but these shrewd crows nearly always managed to pilfer some of his produce. The gardener's skills enabled him to reap an ample harvest without the need to wage war on every pest and predator that his craft attracted.

Woodchester House

V

The young stoats lay silently sleeping in a heap, their well-fed bodies almost filling the nest, so that Gytha scarcely had any space to get away from their constant demands for her milk. The feet and jawbones of young rabbits, fur of voles and feathers of fledgling birds surrounded them and had become incorporated into the nest, for Gytha had already given them their first taste of flesh and blood. Their fur, now the colour of a ripe acorn, had grown longer and thicker, and on the nape it formed a mane. Though their eyes and ears were still not open, they were aware of Gytha's return by the sound of her claws on the alder bark. She had left them to investigate more suitable nest sites on her domain, for she felt the need to move them to new, more roomy quarters where they could begin to exercise their limbs.

As she climbed through the entrance, the kittens rose up together, tottering on their feeble hindlegs to greet her with chirps that only young royal hunters utter, and just as quickly fell back into a heap. She stood astride them and licked each one in turn, but she had no desire to lie down and nurse them. She licked the fur under her arm to soothe the itching caused by biting lice and fleas that multiplied in the warm and humid nest. The kittens began to stir again. The firstborn clambered over his brothers and sisters to nuzzle Gytha's belly, but she shrugged him off before he could find her nipples.

Though Gytha felt a certain unease at the prospect of moving her young from the security of the tree hole, her instinct to do so was strong. Standing over the fidgeting bodies she bent her head and caressed the nape of the quietest bitch. Her jaws closed gently on the mane, and she lifted the kitten out of the nest. Her movements became quick and nervous as she climbed up the side of the tree hole, carrying the kitten to the entrance. Expertly, as if she had performed the manoeuvre many times before, she emerged with her young one held securely in her jaws and head first descended the tree under cover of the ivy. On reaching the ground, she seemed to know exactly where she was going, and she ran off towards the stream.

She crossed a footpath near a stile, over which the young naturalists had climbed only minutes before, and was lost in the lush waterside vegetation of Shortcombe meadow. Now and then she glanced warily about her, the kitten hanging limply from her jaws, as if she was trying to decide the best place to hide her. She had already passed by several rat holes, not even stopping to inspect them. She hesitated before crossing a patch of open grass that rabbits had closely cropped, for she had spotted a grey-backed bird with a long tail swoop low over the meadow and disappear into the hedge along Watery Lane.

The cock sparrowhawk had flown from a fir copse half a mile away and had been on its hedge-hopping hunt for birds that basked in the midday sun. Gytha knew that she must move through the thickest cover she could find in order to keep out of sight of sharp-eyed hawks. All those hook-billed, taloned hunters of the air were to be avoided, for she had seen one of her own sisters carried off by a buzzard as she ran from a hedge into the sunlit stubble one day in late summer. A farm worker had just seen the sparrowhawk slip into Dark Wood. A short while later he heard a cuckoo and saw it fly from its lookout in a wild cherry. It was an ancient belief among country people that as spring arrived the sparrowhawk changed into a cuckoo, and at the end of summer changed back into its former self.

Gytha ran across Watery Lane and, following the hedgerow bounding Oxlease, she made straight for an old pollard willow where she had often rested before she had her kittens. She looked up to see a great tit fly from the tree, where it had made its nest in the decaying, honeycombed heartwood. The great tit, also known as the ox-eye, landed in a nearby ash, churring loudly on seeing the stoat at the foot of the willow. Its glossy, indigo cap and collar, jet black bib, breast and belly streak stood out boldly against its white cheeks and sulphur-yellow underparts, for it was in its breeding plumage.

Gytha walked round to the side of the willow where one of its branches had split and bent to the ground. She ran up it with her usual squirrel-like agility and found the refuge she knew so well. The tree hole was dark and dry and bore the stale smell of birds that had been using it as a roost. It was more spacious than the hollow in the alder. She carried the kitten into a niche that led off from the main chamber and that was covered with fragments of dry, decayed wood. Several feathers lay scattered about, and hidden in the debris were aged, nibbled stones of haws left behind by wood mice. The hollow had been a favourite den of stoats before Gytha was born, for the royal hunter had always been used to living and hunting in trees, just like its primitive progenitors that lived in the tropical forest canopy millions of years ago.

Gytha pawed and sniffed at the wood litter, making a shallow depression in it before laying down the kitten and licking her lovingly. The rapid journey through the cool morning air had put the youngster into a kind of torpor, but Gytha soon revived her. The kitten raised her head and tried to nuzzle her mother's belly, but before she had a chance to find her teats, Gytha left the tree by the same route. She raced along the hedgerow, passing close to the nest of willow warblers. The hen bird, sitting on a thick bed of pheasant feathers, was awaiting the arrival of her first egg and did not sense the rustle of grass blades brushed aside by the anxious stoat. Gytha sped across Watery Lane into the cover of the marshy vegetation, surprising a doe rabbit, which was not in the least perturbed, and bounded after the stoat for several yards before returning to feed. As she ran alongside the stream, she was constantly on her guard against the sparrowhawk, which was in a neighbouring hedgerow plucking alive the small body of a blue tit it held against a branch by the talons of one yellow foot.

On hearing their mother's claws on the alder bark, the kittens called out and became excited at her return, but she only stayed long enough to pick up a second male kitten by his mane and carry him down the tree in the same manner as the first. Again the ox-eye scoffed as it watched her enter the willow, and did not relent until she had vanished into cover to fetch another kitten. Once more she passed within sight of the doe rabbit, and though the scent of it made her more aware of her hunger, her only concern was for her kittens.

Next she took the liveliest of the litter, her firstborn, though even he quickly succumbed to her hold on his mane, and no sooner had she laid him down in the new nest than he huddled closely to the other two kittens to keep warm. On her way to fetch the last kitten she stopped to take a long drink from the stream. Her neck and jaws ached from moving her young, but after the drink she retraced her steps with new vigour. Her progress along the stream was just as decisive as when she had carried the first kitten, such was the stamina so characteristic of her race.

So intent was she to join her young that she was startled by a large black bird that suddenly and silently alighted in the willow. In its massive, hook-tipped bill the carrion crow held a nestling bird. Across the meadow a pair of distressed magpies chackered loudly around their nest, which lacked a sufficiently protective dome of thorny twigs. Since the start of the nesting season the same crow had stolen eggs and preyed upon helpless nestlings. Mistle thrush, song thrush, blackbird and woodpigeon were among those birds that had already suffered the crow's ravages. From its lofty lookout in the top of a pine tree, where it had its nest, or from several other tall trees throughout its spacious territory, it kept a watchful eye on the comings and goings of songbirds. Besides preying on its own kind, the artful gore crow, as the carrion crow was once known, could outwit any tardy rabbit, for fresh, succulent flesh and offal were as alluring as carrion.

The crow tore off the head of the young magpie and gulped it, and after it had swallowed the bald body, it rubbed its bill against a willow branch. It bowed its black head and peered down at the stoat. Its glossy black feathers shimmered purple and indigo in the sun, and the scales covering its legs and feet shone like polished jet. As Gytha stood under the tree looking up at the hunchbacked bird, it sidled along the branch and took flight in the direction of its nest. So cunning was the crow not to give away the whereabouts of its nest that, instead of flying straight to it, it made a devious detour, first to one tree, then took several shorter flights between trees until it became hidden from view in the conifer.

Gytha carried the last kitten aloft, and as soon as she climbed into the hollow the kittens smelled her and scrambled over one another in their eagerness to find her warm belly. She lay down in the nest and subdued them with soft chirping sounds.

The ox-eye flew into its nest hole with horsehair trailing from its bill, for it had been gathering moulted hairs from around the huge feet of the shire horse from Fawkes' farm that grazed in Oxlease. Ruddock, dunnock and chaffinch, which now brooded their nestlings along Watery Lane, had also collected the same hairs to make their felted nest linings. The gore crow, perching astride the horse's back, had plucked at the long, loose hairs of the great mane with deft movements of its clumsy-looking bill. It had even pulled out some of the tail hairs to add to its thick nest lining.

Gytha lay suckling her kittens in their new home. She ran her tongue over her sore pads to soothe them. She felt hungry after the effort of moving her litter, who now slept with their bellies full of her milk. Not even the shrewd crow perching in an ash at the edge of Dark Wood saw her slip from the willow and bound along the hedge in the direction of Watery Lane. She crouched at the stream and lapped the cool spring water, her forepaws placed in the footprint of a badger, which had drunk from the same spot the previous night. She wiped one paw against her wet, white chin and rubbed it repeatedly over her muzzle. At the same time she had her eyes trained on the hazel hedge bordering the lane, a short distance down from the spring water drinking trough. She could discern the hen robin that had just left her nestlings in the bank. In her bill she held one of the white sacs of excrement she had removed from the nest.

The nestlings were not allowed to foul the nest, for as each parent delivered food it frequently picked up a dropping, freshly deposited on the edge, and carried it off. The robin that Gytha watched so intently from the cover of some rushes wiped her bill against a hazel twig, leaving the gelatinous bag of waste adhering to it. In this way, not only did the parents keep the nest spotless, but ensured that its whereabouts remained hidden from would-be predators.

The robin spied the stoat stealing along the stream, and flew across the lane to her nest, calling out urgently, so that the nestlings huddled closer together and pressed their stubby-feathered bodies against the thick horsehair lining. Gytha ran into the blackthorn thicket that grew behind the red-brick barn and where long-tailed tits often nested. She felt again the pangs of hunger. She stood on her hindlegs, resting one paw on the bush's black stem, and peered up into the thorny branches. With ears pricked and dark eyes shining she was alert to the faintest sound and slightest movement. Her keen nostrils dilated and contracted as they tested the small eddies that wafted almost imperceptible scents through the thicket. As she stretched up on her hindfeet to get a closer look at a blackbird's nest, the cock bird returned with food for the fledglings. He saw the white throat of the royal hunter standing out against the dark stems and flew panic-stricken into the lane with his characteristic alarm rattle, holding fast on to the worms in his bill. Gytha gazed up into the branches and watched several wing feathers gyrate to the ground before climbing up to the nest.

The whole hedgerow and lane between the red-brick barn and the spring water trough became noisy with the cries of the two parents and other birds that nested in the vicinity. Above the alarm calls a willow warbler trilled its incessant rippling phrases. Needle-sharp thorns stabbed at Gytha as she climbed up to the nest a few feet above the ground. By the time she reached it two of the five fledglings, encouraged by the constant calls of their parents, had struggled out and fluttered unsteadily among the branches.

She squeezed between one of the crotches that supported the nest and killed two fledglings, each with a single fatal bite into its thin skull. She struck out at a third bird as it tottered on the edge of the nest and pulled it towards her, skilfully dispatching it in the same way. The cock bird and the two surviving fledglings looked on from their various perches, and the hen bird flew agitatedly into the lane, piping forlornly as she witnessed the slaughter. Her earlier attempt at rearing young had failed, for magpies had taken her eggs before she had a chance to brood them.

Gytha licked up the warm, dark blood that flowed from the fledgling's ruptured vessels, and grasping it by the neck she carried it off. She hid her prey beneath some trailing vines of blithytwine that reached down to the ground, and amid cries from the distraught parents she returned twice more to the nest to retrieve the remaining two fledglings. In the cover of the blithytwine, she gorged the tender flesh and entrails of two of the fledglings, saving the third to take to her nest. After she had eaten, only the beak and feet and a few feathers remained to reveal that a predator had passed that way.

The young blackbirds were not the first spring fledglings Gytha had taken from the hedgerows. Since she had tasted avian flesh as a newly weaned kitten she had grown to relish it. No sooner had she learned to kill for herself, than she followed her instinct to hunt birds, which she inherited from her forest-dwelling forebears. She emerged from the curtain of blithytwine with the fledgling in her jaws, to the renewed rattle of the robin. Her only thought now was for her kittens. She glanced over her shoulder across the meadow, but did not see the carrion crow standing sentinel over the hedgerow. A swallow from the red-brick barn flew low over the grass and spotted the stoat as she hurried back to her kittens, and the pair of blackbirds again foraged for their two surviving young.

Gytha entered the willow tree den so silently that the kittens were slow to stir. But when she laid her kill outside the entrance to the nest chamber they woke and climbed over one another to find her warm, milk-laden teats. For a while she lay suckling them, then she raised herself up on her forelegs and began to heave. In the darkness of the new nursery she felt with her long, sensitive whiskers and moist nose for each expectant mouth, which she fed with the disgorged flesh of the fledglings she had eaten.

She used her long, agile tongue to deliver morsels, ensuring that each kitten received an equal portion of the partially digested, nutritious food she had expended so much energy in procuring. The kittens relished the warm vomit that tasted so much of their mother, and when she had emptied her stomach they all cried out for more. She felt pangs of hunger again and was tempted to eat the remaining fledgling, but first she satisfied the demands of her kittens by suckling them again. As they fed, she licked them clean of the excrement they still voided inside the nest, and when they could draw no more milk from her and had fallen asleep, she began to eat the young blackbird.

The young naturalists stopped at the spring water trough in Watery Lane. The older lad gave his friend the tin egg box to hold, and crouching down at the trough, he bailed out the cool water with tightly cupped hands and lifted them to his mouth to drink. As he swallowed, he felt an ice-cold sensation pass down into his stomach. When he had finished, he held the precious egg box while his friend bent down and immersed his mouth in the crystal clear water, hesitantly sucking it in through pursed lips. As he drank, he looked down through the water and noticed magnified grains of white quartz sand, yellow clay and limestone fragments, which made up the so-called Cotswold sand, lying on the bottom of the trough. Besides the usual fascination that water had for young eyes, his were drawn to inanimate rock and the petrified remnants of past life. However, he was too young to understand that the roe-like rock had its origin in a former subtropical sea, or that the clear quartz sand was once its wave-washed beach and the product of the erosion by primeval rivers of even more ancient mountains.

After they had quenched their thirst, the boys made their way home. That morning they had found the nests of moorhen, willow warbler, whitethroat and wren, chaffinch and linnet. They had taken one egg from each nest, either before the hen bird had laid a full clutch or before she had begun to brood them, for they were naturalists enough to know such things. So plentiful were birds in this pastoral parish that the boys' harmless depredations had no lasting detrimental effect on their numbers.

More than a century before, when the bird life was even more abundant and diverse, there were two young naturalists living at Woodchester House who collected not only the eggs but the skins of birds. The two brothers, Henry and Frank Housman, cousins of A E Housman, the classical scholar and poet, went around with an older lad who lived at the Old Priory, which at that time was called the Farms. He would carry a shotgun to shoot specimens, which he would show the boys how to stuff. There were few birds living in Longtree in those days that did not also stand stuffed in glass cases in the Housman brothers' home museum, including such rarities as red-backed shrike, corncrake and short-eared owl.

Remains of the old parish church

VI

A breeze, born of a westerly wind beating up the vale, stirred the beech leaves above Oxlease and ruffled the feathers of a tawny owl that looked out over the moonlit meadow. Many millions of years before the birth of vale and wold, the same wind blew over a primeval sea, whipping up waves that lapped its coral reefs, whose petrified remains lay beneath Selsley Common. As the church clock chimed midnight, Gytha, feeling the nudging noses of her kittens, stretched herself alongside them and let down her milk. The firstborn sucked greedily, and when he could get no more milk, he clambered over his nest mates and clamped his jaws on another nipple, which one of his sleepy sisters had just let go.

Gytha, who was now even more perceptive to the needs of her young, placed one outspread forepaw on the young dog's head and pushed him away, allowing the bitch to feed again. The firstborn responded to her reproach by raising one of his paws in defiance, and with jaws agape to show a full set of milk teeth, he made a kind of chirping noise. When they had taken their fill, two of the kittens crept out of the nest, one behind the other, and squatted down to add their dark, elongated scats to those that had already accumulated in a corner of the tree hollow. Now they no longer performed their toilet in the sleeping area, nor relied on their mother to keep them clean.

Gytha drew away from the kittens, and reclining in her favourite corner began to groom herself. She licked her thinning belly hair and tender teats, as was her habit after each suckle. Then she moistened her forepaws with her tongue and rubbed them over her ears and muzzle, removing minute particles of soil from her fur and long whiskers. Next she cleaned her paws, fanning out her toes to probe between the pads with her fine, chisel-shaped incisors and the tip of her tongue.

The church clock's tenor tones signalled the beginning of the first hour of another day as Gytha left the nest and climbed down the pollard willow. She stood at the base of the tree and watched the moon appear from behind scudding, inky clouds. From Dark Wood a tawny owl gave a single, short shriek. At the edge of Oxlease a doe rabbit thumped the ground with her hindfeet, and her young ones scurried back to their burrow, their white scuts showing up in the moonlight. From the shadows of the beeches the owl glided down from its lookout and took a quarter-grown rabbit as it nibbled the dewy grass. The owl's feather-fringed talons closed on the quivering animal and quickly ended its brief life. The owl gripped the flaccid skin of the rabbit's back with both feet and carried it off along the woodland edge. With a score of wingbeats the night hunter bore its burdensome quarry to its nest hole in an ash tree and laid it at the feet of its fledglings.

Now that the hedgerows were in full leaf and the undergrowth and herbage around the wood were growing lush, it was more difficult for the tawny owl to find voles and wood mice, but young rabbits feeding at night at the edge of the wood became easy prey. Nature's perfect timing never failed to ensure that the spring flush of vegetation arrived to give sustenance to the growing numbers of rabbits and rodents. These insatiable herbivores in turn had their young in abundance at the season when the hunters of night and day were rearing their offspring.

The doe rabbit whose youngster the tawny owl had carried off huddled in her hole, and the three surviving ones snuggled up close to her. Already she, the sole survivor of a litter born the previous summer, had given birth to five kittens on the first day of spring. All five had been dug out by a badger before they had even tasted grass. Soon, as her enlarged dewlap showed, she would give birth to more young, some of whom in infancy, youth and adulthood would become the prey of stoat, weasel, badger, fox, owl and hawk.

Gytha nosed among the rabbit-grazed grass growing alongside the drystone wall that bordered Dark Wood, and crouching down she left a small string of scented scats. She stood on all fours with her back straight, head and neck stretched forward and tail tip jerking. All her senses were alerted to the still night. Her twitching nostrils caught the mixed odours of the marshy meadow where the springs rose. Horsetail and rush, and the fresh spoil pushed up by moles each gave their own smells to the mild night air. But above them all she could smell the spring water, and at one of her favourite drinking places she savoured it, under cover of spreading meadowsweet foliage. While she drank she heard the tiny popping noises of air bubbles that the water carried with it as it burst from the clayey ground. She retraced her steps to Dark Wood and began to hunt for wood mice, which sometimes took refuge in mole runs alongside the drystone wall. Her body was now as trim and lithe as it had been before she carried her young. Even in the dim light of the moon her pelt shone, for it was now in its summer prime.

Intent on pursuing a wood mouse through the mole's tunnel, she did not hear the playful bickering of badger cubs up in the beech wood. The young badgers followed close behind the sow as she scratched and rooted for beetles and earthworms. Each time she made a find she encouraged her charges to take the prey by quietly grunting. Now the cubs were learning by her example how to forage for themselves. They were still too young and inexpert to tackle larger meat than these lowly woodland scavengers, and it would be some time before they learned to dig out a nest of young rabbits.

The sow was well versed in such hunting, and she soon located a kindle of rabbits that an inexperienced doe was nursing in a shallow stop. Through a foot of soil her searching snout detected the smell of the doe and her kittens. She dug vertically down through the earth, her long claws tearing and tugging at fibrous roots and scattering soil and pieces of limestone in all directions. The doe, on hearing the ground moving above her, abandoned her babies and bolted from the burrow. The badger broke through the roof of the nest chamber and pulled out the baby rabbits with her raking claws, and after nipping each one in the neck, she placed them under the snuffling noses of her cubs.

In the earthy darkness of the mole run Gytha squirmed and wriggled, her slim body almost filling the tunnel, so that her pelt brushed against its smooth sides. Her supple, spring-like spine and short limbs fitted her perfectly for such underground hunting. The long, tactile hairs that sprouted from the top of her head above her eyes, the paired clusters of hairs beneath her chin, and the long whiskers on each side of her muzzle enabled her to judge the size of the burrow she explored. Any burrow she could squeeze her head through would enable her lithe body to follow. Particles of soil fell from the roof and slithered off the glossy guard hairs of her back as she twisted along the winding passage. Though soil fell around her ears, none got inside, for a gristly flap of skin and a fringe of long, coarse, backward-projecting hairs sealed off the hearing canal.

She came to a junction in the underground maze where the wood mouse's scent lingered, and she felt a sudden shower of soil against her face. The wood mouse, only a few lengths ahead, was frantically trying to make its escape through a plug of excavated earth, which the mole had formed into a small hill. Momentarily she lost track of the scent as her nostrils became covered in soil.

The wood mouse broke through the earth mound and into the moonlit meadow. It sped over the grass in long leaps and bounds towards the drystone wall and slipped between the mossy limestone blocks.

Gytha emerged from the mole-run, shook her head and shoulders, and picking up the wood mouse's scent once more, followed exactly on the trail of the fleeing rodent. When she arrived at the spot where her quarry had taken refuge, she found the space between the stones too narrow to get through. The wood mouse crouched in a cavity surrounded by stones so closely fitting that, despite Gytha's ability to squeeze through other parts of the wall, it knew it was safe. Its palpitating heart began to recover, and its excited nostrils became calm as it listened through its large ears to the royal hunter leave the wall.

The sky was now cloudless, and further out in the meadow ragged rows of molehills showed up in the light of the full moon. One of the tawny owls, digesting its last meal and blinking drowsily, watched the spot where a new earth mound was slowly growing. Hidden in a tunnel beneath the rising soil, a mole levered up another load of earth through the shallow shaft with one of his massive shovel-like forepaws. The canny old male took great care not to show himself to the moon. Though his poor sight could discern no shape or form, he could sense the moon's pale light through the spaces of loose soil as he heaved upwards, and his highly tuned nose probed the surface to take in the cool, odorous air. He made a hurried about-turn and scurried back along the loamy corridor, his flexible snout constantly casting around in search of prey.

The grey velvet-coated hunter of the underworld possessed an appetite equalled only by that of his close cousin the shrew. An earthworm that had crawled through the grass a moment before returned to its burrow and dropped headlong into the tunnel recently dug by the mole. Before he could gather his primitive senses together, the voracious insectivore grabbed it with his primitive teeth. He held the wriggling, slimy worm between his horny-skinned palms and searched for the head end with his finely whiskered snout. Despite his hunger, the ount, as some country folk called him, was particular in his eating habits. As he guided the head end of the worm into his narrow mouth, he wiped away the slimy covering with the comb of hairs fringing the inner edge of his forepaws. When he had chewed his way along to the worm's gut he took care not to contaminate his meal with the earthy contents that oozed out, and cleaned away the silty, sandy sludge.

At regular times during day and night the mole patrolled and hunted through his labyrinthine domain. From time immemorial, long before the first farmers began to clear the forest and till the soil, the mole's ancestors ploughed beneath the wold. Then, as now, the mole preferred to make its home in the fertile soil of broad-leaved woodland, where its mounds became natural nurseries for the seedlings of herbs and trees. Royal hunter and weasel had always lived close alongside the mole, for each took advantage of its underground highways, using them both as refuges from enemies and as places in which to pursue prey that sheltered there. Although the mole still lived in woodland, it burrowed out into the surrounding pasture in search of earthworms and insects that grew fat on the cattle-enriched ground.

The noise the mole made as he gobbled the worm was just one of the many hidden sounds made by the night's hunters. Gytha crawled through a gap in the drystone wall and ran high on her toes through the shadows of beech and bramble that the moon cast on the woodland floor. Following close alongside the wall, she heard the sounds of ground beetles foraging in the leaf litter, and even the noises made by snails rasping algae from fallen branches. She trod stealthily, her muzzle set close to the ground and her sharp ears wavering independently to pick up every small squeal of shrew and vole, rustle of leaf and snap of twig. She stopped in her tracks, and straining her neck forward, watched and listened to a stirring among the ivy that straggled over the woodland floor. As she drew nearer to the spot, her nose singled out the faint scent of mole from among the stronger smell of mouldering beech leaves.

A female mole had surfaced through a pop-hole to gather dry leaves for her nest. In the shadows Gytha clearly saw the dark form scurry down the hole, but the smell the velvety animal left behind did not excite her nostrils, for the flesh of the mole, like its cousin the shrew, she found rather distasteful, and would eat it only as a last resort. The solitary young-bearing ount scuttled along the winding burrow of her fortress, following her own scent trail back to the nest chamber. Here she pushed the withered leaves into the bundle of dry litter that would shortly cradle her young.

Gytha explored around the roots of an old beech beneath which wood mice had burrowed, dislodging a snail that was browsing on the powdery green algae encrusting the moist bark. Soon she fell upon the scent of a wood mouse that had left its hole to forage among the leaf litter, under cover of ivy and bramble, where it was safer from the searching eyes and ears of the tawny owl. The long-tailed mouse with large nocturnal eyes and ears crouched amongst the leaves, chewing on a black beetle that had wandered from a badger's dung pit, where it had lived as a grub. The wood mouse raised its head, cocked its ears, and stared through the darkness with its black, bulbous eyes. Its quivering nose winded the stoat just in time. Gytha sprang at the fleeing mouse, but the long-legged rodent was too quick for her. With kangaroo-like leaps it escaped her clutches and took refuge beneath the beech roots where she could not follow.

Now Gytha hunted through rabbit runs and sent several rabbits rushing for their burrows. Others sat up on their haunches and turned their heads to wind her as she streaked past in pursuit of a half-grown doe. She chased it almost as far as the badger sets and caught up with it as it cowered in the grass. A badger, removing soiled bedding from its nest chamber, heard the stoated rabbit squeal and lifted its muddy snout to scent the royal hunter and her prey. Gytha leapt on to the rabbit's back, and seizing it by the neck, bit through skin and muscle until the tips of her canines met its backbone. For several minutes the rabbit struggled and tried to throw her off, but she hung on, biting harder and deeper. Only when she felt its body go limp did she relax her vice-like grip, and she began to lick up the blood that the failing heart feebly pumped. The rabbit was more than two and a half times her own weight, so she had to gather all her strength to hide it before it became easy prey for fox or badger.

Gytha was on the threshold of the most strenuous stage in her life, for from now on she would need to summon all her energy and hunting prowess in order to satisfy the growing appetites of her kittens. When she had covered almost a third of the distance to her den, she stopped to rest and to renew her hold on her quarry. A badger lumbered down the bank, made from many decades of digging, and began to snuffle in the grass for earthworms. She listened to the noisy creature as it chanced upon the trail she and her prey had made through the grass, but the sound of her own racing heart seemed louder.

When she reached the pollard willow she once more changed her hold on the rabbit and hauled it up to her den in the same way that a leopard will protect its kill from other predators by hiding it in a tree. The kittens, whose ears had begun to open during the night, were now even more alert to the approach of their mother as she scaled the tree, and they started to creep from the nest when they heard her enter the hollow. She lay the rabbit down and greeted her kittens by licking them and making low-pitched warbling sounds, to which they responded with chirps. Some of them were eager to find her teats, but others, including the firstborn, showed more interest in the smell of the still warm rabbit.

Gytha began to bite into the side of the rabbit's neck just below one ear, where she had dealt the death blow. She tore away pieces of fur and skin until she had exposed the tender neck muscles, and these she sliced through with her shearing molar teeth, so enabling her kittens to taste the blood-gorged tissues. She bit through the back of the young skull and ate out the brain, allowing them to take some, for this was the royal hunter's choicest of delicacies. When she had eaten, her stomach was bulging with chunks of muscle, furred skin and liquified brain, all bathed in congealed blood. This would sustain her until sunrise, and would help to replenish the milk that her kittens still demanded, for although they enjoyed flesh and blood, the warm, wholesome food of her own body was still a great comforter and fattener. She licked the kittens as they sucked the last flow of milk from her tired belly, then she fell asleep with them. While they slept other hunters were awake.

In the old churchyard the diminutive doe weasel left her five young to hunt voles in their runs beneath the drystone wall. She had dropped her kittens three days before in a den below the clothier's ornate tombstone. The nest was lined with dried grass and the fur of field voles, and its entrance was only wide enough to allow through the wiry doe weasel. The weasel was a descendant of those same animals that almost two thousand years ago had lived among the foundations of the first Roman villa of Woodchester. The inhabitants of the villa encouraged weasels to live alongside them, for they knew they kept down the mice that lived in their corn ricks and granary.

The solitary barn owl, which had returned during the night to this same quarter of the parish, listened and watched from its perch among the ivied remains of the old Norman church. It heard the grass-rustling vole flushed from its hole by the weasel, and turned its pale face towards the sound. Within the short space of time that it took the parish church clock to chime the quarter-hour, the owl flew down from its roost and took the vole. As the weasel surfaced from the vole's burrow she saw the owl's talons swing forward, pendulum-like, and brush the grass. She also heard the vole's brief squeal and felt the rush of air roused by the bird's braking wings, and she retreated into the vole's burrow.

In the yew tree overhanging the churchyard wall the hen goldcrest brooded her nestlings, and the cock bird roosted close against the trunk, oblivious of the hunting owl. The blackbird that had lost some of her first brood sat on her second clutch, and at the edge of the millpond the moorhen whose first clutch had been taken by the lame dog fox sat on another seven eggs. In the middle of the pond a trout snapped up a moth as it struggled on the surface, causing moonlight-reflecting ripples to pass over the still water and gently rock the lily leaves.

The barn owl left its feeding place and once more quartered the churchyard. As it flew over the drystone wall into the garden of the Old Priory it saw the sinuous outline of the doe weasel in the grass, and continued on a straight course towards the tussocky grass bordering the stream in Shortcombe meadow. The weasel did not waver from her hunt for voles, and neither saw nor heard the silent white owl. Soon she chanced upon the trail of a vole and sent it running into the open, where a large expanse of mown turf marked the site of the Roman pavement.

In the corner of Oxlease where the red-brick barn stood, a group of cows lay ruminating. A foraging hedgehog heard the sounds of the cows chewing the cud and smelled the droplets of milk that a shorthorn's full udder exuded. In the parish, as in other parts of the hundred, there was a belief that a hedgehog took milk from a cow's teats as eagerly as suckling hedgepigs took milk from their mother. The hedgehog approached the reclining shorthorn, grunting and snuffling, and the cow nonchalantly turned her head to watch it lick up beads of milk that clung to the grass blades beneath her turgid teats. The cow paid no attention to the hedgehog as it pushed its wet snout beneath her taut udder to seek the warm, sweet milk that trickled on to the grass.

The Lawn horse chestnuts

VII

As spring gave way to summer there were few inhabitants of Woodchester who were as receptive to the natural events and seasonal changes that took place around them as Jim Hammond. Milkman, ploughman and general farm hand at Fawkes' farm, Jim had noted on his daily milk round up Selsley Road the horse chestnut trees come into leaf and flower.

It was Jim's hands that Henry Payne, the stained glass artist who once lived at St Loe's House on Amberley, had immortalised in his figure of St George in the memorial chapel at Notre Dame de Lorette National Cemetery, Arras, the largest of all the First World War cemeteries on the Western Front. Harry Payne, as he was better known, had often used local people as models for his cartoons. He had sketched Jim's handsome hands for his figure of St George, shown holding a sword in his left hand and a lance in his right, which occupies one of six stained glass lancet windows illuminating the chapel. This gift from the Imperial War Graves Commission was intended as a token of gratitude to the French for their assistance in maintaining the graves of British soldiers who fell in France – and for their generous free grants of land for the British cemeteries and memorials.

Now that May was more than three-quarters gone, the horse chestnuts growing behind the high wall of the Lawn were almost past their prime. The pyramidal flower spikes stood erect amid the large palmate leaves like so many ornate, white candelabra, which accounted for the common country name of candle tree. On the road, alongside the narrow strip of long grass growing at the foot of the wall, lay shallow, wind-blown drifts of rose- and lemon-tinted white petals with other exhausted parts of the flowers, like so much confetti. High up in the sunlit branches the youngest flowers lured honeybees and humbledores from their hives and holes to gather nectar and pollen for growing broods.

A few yards further up the hill, on the opposite side of the road, Lilian Cashmore from Larchgrove Cottage threw handfuls of weeds to her fowls in the adjoining pound. She watched the hens run to peck greedily at the greenstuff, for she knew that the nutritious groundsel and chickweed were as vital to their health as the insects they caught amongst the thick ivy overhanging the pound wall. Her skilful husbandry, learned during her early country upbringing, was rewarded with russet-shelled eggs whose yolks were as orange as the marigolds that grew in her garden in high summer.

In a coop in one corner of the pound a broody Rhode Island Red kept close watch over her chicks as they sunned themselves in the dusty earth, or scratched at it with ungainly, reptile-like feet. The eggs from which the chicks had hatched were laid by the broody hen and others of the same generation of home-bred birds, all of whom had been impregnated by the same dawn-declaring rooster. Lilian had selected with her expert eye each well-formed egg. The birds she reared from this brood of ten would gradually replace the old hens that went off lay, which would then become meat for the table.

In another garden on the same hillside a beekeeper stood by his hives. He watched the entrance to a white cottage hive that had swarmed the previous May. He recalled how he had been in poor health that year and unable to take the swarm before it found a hollow elm. He knew that this hive was headed by a queen in her second summer and nearing full lay. He also knew, through many years of following his craft, which flowers and tree blossoms his bees were working. Over the last month he had watched foragers return with nectar and pollen harvested from a host of plants and trees that grew in his well-stocked garden and around the hillside.

Crouching by the hive the beekeeper watched workers leave and return. Many alighted on the flight board bearing pollen loads of pale pastel colours, brushed from the blossoms of sycamore, hawthorn and apple. He noted too those bees that were working the horse chestnut flowers, for they carried brick-red pollen on their hindlegs. Some with empty pollen baskets landed heavily, and these he knew had honey sacs brimful of nectar. A look of contentment passed over his weather-beaten face, for he could tell from the bees' behaviour that the first honey flow of the season was underway. He had learned from his father the rudiments of beekeeping, and throughout his long and active life he had acquired a vast store of bee lore by working closely alongside the gentle honeybee.

Along the footpath that led across the pasture known as Villa Field the young naturalists strolled in search of jackdaw nestlings to rear as pets. Some weeks before, one of the boys had climbed an oak tree, and putting his hand into the nest hole counted four eggs. He had noted when the hen went down on her clutch, had reckoned the time of brooding, and had seen both parents bring food to the nest. As the boys walked they spoke together with an accent that was as soft and pleasing to the ear as sunlit Cotswold stone is to the eye. Despite all their knowledge of the wealth of wildlife in the parish, there were some creatures, like the royal hunter and weasel, whose breeding habits were so secretive that the inquisitive youngsters had never been able to discover their dens.

Almost half a mile to the west of Villa Field, the beeches of Dark Wood displayed gradations of green that would have eluded the palette of the most able watercolourist. In the pollard willow, just below the wood, Gytha reclined aside from her kittens. She had finished suckling them shortly after the church clock struck noon. She licked clean her sore teats, around which the fine, cream-coloured fur had been removed by the kittens' grasping mouths, stopping now and then to listen to their melodious chirping. Each day that she suckled them she felt their jaws grip more strongly, and their needle-sharp teeth would often make her wince.

The kittens grew sturdier, their dumpy bodies drawing sustenance from the flesh of rabbit, vole, bird and Gytha's milk. The mane on their napes by which she had carried them from the natal nest had disappeared, as the bracken-brown fur of their upper parts had grown longer. But still their tails had not yet grown the black tassel that set the royal hunter apart from its smaller cousin. Over the last few days the eyes of all but the smallest male had opened, but in the darkness of the tree hollow they still relied on their other senses to locate Gytha and each other. They had developed stronger limbs and moved rapidly in small, jerky steps, stretching out their bodies at full length, so exercising the muscles and sinews of their spines.

Gytha moved over to her young and gently nuzzled them. The firstborn lifted his head, gave a loud chirp, and grabbed hold of the underside of her neck. She responded with a loud threatening cackle and tried to shake off the grasping kitten, who eventually released his hold and lay on his back with legs sticking up in the air. He rolled over on to all fours and began to follow Gytha, catching hold of her tail with his jaws and forepaws. Suddenly she turned round and with a hiss of disapproval cuffed the kitten across the muzzle. The young dog put up a paw in anticipation of a further blow, but Gytha had left the nest, and, probing with his moist nose, he rejoined his littermates.

Gytha stood alert at the entrance to the nest. She put her head out and peered upwards into the branches to watch the ox-eyes return with food for their nestlings, for the presence of the royal hunter in the same tree had not made the birds desert their nest. So swiftly did she leave the tree that the ox-eyes' cries were short-lived. She ran along the edge of Oxlease towards Dark Wood, and at the same spot as earlier in the day winded the same doe rabbit intent on filling her belly with lush, milk-making grass, for in a well-concealed stop she had six sucklings. Gytha soon spied the doe and took cover behind a beech stump, crouching down in the ivy that enmeshed its decaying remains.

Overhead, a loud clapping of woodpigeons' wings and the raucous chatter of magpies broke the silence of the wood. She stole round the tree stump and watched the feeding rabbit. The air in the wood was still, yet her sensitive nose found another smell, far stronger than that of rabbit. Out of the corner of one eye she saw the dog stoat Aethelwald. Now that she needed to hunt more often to satisfy the hunger of her fast-growing kittens, chance encounters with him became more frequent. Ever since she had moved her young, he spent more time in this quarter of his domain, lying up in the warren and feasting on the burgeoning rabbit population.

The doe rabbit stopped grazing at the clearing and bounded into a bramble patch. Aethelwald raised himself up to his full stature and cackled at Gytha across a distance spanned by the boughs of a single beech. Gytha cowered timidly, though held her ground, cackling softly through slightly bared teeth. Aethelwald leapt on top of a felled tree on which badger cubs had gambolled the previous night. He ran along its length, pausing now and then to sniff at traces of the badgers' strong scent. When he reached the end of the hundred-year-old trunk he stood with his powerful back arched, his bushy brush waving slowly from side to side and his broad muzzle sweeping the air for Gytha's scent. But she had gone as silently as the rabbit, for her only concern was to hunt for her kittens.

The cries of a jenny wren marked the route Gytha had taken past a nestful of feathered youngsters concealed among the bared roots of an upturned beech that had been blown over in a gale. A cock pheasant, watching out for one of his harem, called 'korrk-korrk' on spotting the stoat cross the clearing. Gytha stopped in her tracks and glanced back over her shoulder to see if Aethelwald was following her, but he had climbed into one of his favourite trees to bask in the sun and survey his patch. She came to a clearing in the wood where the warmth of the sun made the wild garlic exude its powerful, pungent scent. She squatted close to the same spot she had scent-marked several days before, and listened to the deep drone of a bumblebee. The smell of the wild garlic masked more delicate scents than her discerning nose sought. She ran with her muzzle skimming the ground, making a meandering path over the clearing and pausing to pick up new and pleasant smells left behind by birds and wood mice. Soon she found a trail that led beneath some brambles from which a hen pheasant had recently emerged.

No one could say with certainty when pheasants first nested in Woodchester. Some say the Romans, who laid its famous mosaic pavement, which features the oriental ring-necked pheasant, brought over the exotic gamebirds to breed and fatten in coops, as was their custom in their native Italy, and that some of them escaped into the countryside. Others think the birds didn't arrive until after the Norman Conquest, when Edward Earl of Salisbury, a follower of the Conqueror, farmed Woodchester before the Maltravers family held the manor. In recent times the landed gentry employed men with an intimate knowledge of birds and beasts under whose care the pheasant spread far and wide over the wold. The pheasants that frequented Woodchester were descendants of birds raised on keepered estates further afield.

Gytha stood by a pheasant's nest, which was a mere scrape in the leaf litter, containing ten unbrooded eggs. This was not the first time she had set eyes on pheasants' eggs. Even as a kitten in the nest she had tasted those eggs brought back by her mother. In the early spring, before she had given birth to her young, she had robbed the nests of wild duck, mistle thrush and lapwing, for like all members of the weasel tribe, the royal hunter was particularly fond of eggs. She clambered over the clutch, sniffing at the still warm, olive-brown eggs. Though under cover of the brambles, she overcame a desire to savour one of the eggs and followed her instinct to carry it off to one of her caches. She lay on her side at the edge of the nest, and arching her neck over the egg, she rolled it out under her chin, using her forepaws to guide and steady it.

She turned over on to her back, cradling the egg against her chest with her chin and forepaws, her hindquarters bent forwards so that her hindpaws touched her cheeks and her tail brushed the crown of her head. But, however hard she tried, she could not get a grip with her canines on the narrower end of the egg. Unlike the smaller one of the partridge, the pheasant's egg was too large for her gape. Then, turning on to her front again, she started to push the egg away from the nest with her nose, guiding it with her forepaws. She rolled it out of the brambles and on to a rabbit run, travelling almost as fast as a man walks. She checked it constantly as it wavered to left and right from its intended course, increasing or decreasing her pace according to the slope of the ground. Several times, when she met an obstruction in her path such as a branch or piece of limestone, she would lift the egg over or manoeuvre it round the obstacle using her nose and forepaws. By the time she had reached the boundary of Oxlease, she had covered a distance of almost fifty human paces, and yet there was not even a hairline crack in the egg, which she pushed into a hole beneath the roots of the pollard willow where she had her young.

As she returned to fetch another egg, a pair of magpies spied her from their lookout on the drystone wall. The sharp-witted birds chackered and flew over to a beech tree near to the place they had first seen Gytha roll the egg out from the brambles. She saw and heard the noisy birds, but did not waver from the shortest route leading from her larder to the pheasant's nest. More skilfully than before she secured another egg and pushed it along a new path, out of sight of the magpies. But while she was away they stole beneath the brambles, and she arrived back at the nest to find they had cracked open five of the eggs and sucked out the yolky contents. She heard the magpies chacker nearby, waiting their turn, and she quickly licked up the traces of yolk from inside the empty shells before rolling away another egg.

Reclining on the branch of an oak Aethelwald surveyed the field where the springs rose. He watched the swallows taking insects that the midday sun roused from the marshy ground. He lay stretched out along the branch, twenty feet above the ground, his bushy tail hanging over the edge and his forepaws crossed over one another beneath his chin. His well-groomed coat glistened in the sun, for it was in its summer prime. His gaze was fixed on a bramble patch at the edge of Dark Wood, and his ears were directed towards the sounds coming from within. Suddenly, out of the brambles rushed a royal hunter pursued by a rabbit. It covered the ground in curious leaps and bounds, unlike the normal gait of a stoat. The fleeing animal was a yearling bitch who had a litter in the drystone wall. While out hunting for nestling rabbits she had been surprised by a nursing doe who had given chase in defence of her young. The stoat was no match for the rabbit, for she had no forelegs. Even a royal hunter with four sound limbs had been known to be mauled by an enraged doe rabbit.

Aethelwald raised his head and opened his jaws in a wide yawn, and after he closed them, the left margin of his white-edged muzzle became rucked up by a worn lower canine tooth, so that his noble mask took on a one-sided leer. He watched the bitch stoat with no forelegs propel her lithe frame over the grass with powerful thrusts of her muscular hindlegs, her tail held out straight behind to steady herself. When she reached the drystone wall she stood up bold and erect, and looked back to see her adversary retreating into the brambles.

The crippled stoat was one of Gytha's siblings who, soon after becoming independent of her mother, had been trapped in a gin set for rabbits. The iron jaws had closed high up on her forelegs and had almost severed them, so that it was not difficult for her to bite her way out of the trap. Unlike her able-bodied littermates, she had grown up to be more wary and less adventurous, and so had survived long enough to bear and give birth to more of Aethelwald's line. She stood still against the wall, her cream belly blending with the limestone. She lowered her muzzle to the ground to sniff at the spot where Gytha had left her scent mark, and, soon finding a way between the stone blocks, she vanished inside the wall. Though the hunting grounds of both bitch stoats overlapped, there was no competition between them, for while one hunted the other suckled her young or rested.

Aethelwald climbed down from his lookout. He paused to leave his scent on a fallen branch and made his way down the side of the meadow towards Watery Lane. He peered up into the hazel branches, but only heard the willow warblers interrupt their search for food to call out in alarm. Their nest among the brier-bound tussocks still remained safe from the sight and hearing of the royal hunter and weasel, for the nestlings kept silent when their parents were hunting for insects. Aethelwald watched out for signs of movement among the leaves, but the warblers had moved on to draw off another predator from the vicinity of their nest.

A doe weasel hunting along the hedgerow winded the stoat and went to ground in a wood mouse burrow. Aethelwald descended the bank of Watery Lane by the same claw-scored path a badger had taken the previous night, crossed the lane in three bounds, and leapt up the opposite bank, his black tail tip waving and showing above the herbage enough to be noticed by a farm labourer. Aethelwald pricked his ears at the sudden shrill sound coming from further along the lane, for he had heard the same sound many times before uttered by rabbits that had been his quarry.

He stood on his haunches at the top of the bank, his inquisitive head pointing towards the source of the sound. The farm labourer again mimicked the squeal of a frightened rabbit by drawing in short rapid breaths through pursed lips held between his calloused forefingers. This was an age-old custom of gamekeepers and hunters to lure stoats and weasels from cover. Aethelwald felt uneasy and was drawn no further towards the familiar sound. He had seen his mother enticed out of a hedge by a rabbit catcher and killed by a spray of shot. His curiosity ebbed and he turned tail and fled into the safety of the long grass alongside the stream in Shortcombe. In the time it took Gytha to retrieve and cache the last pheasant's egg, he had reached the eastern edge of his domain by the brook.

The Lawn

Dark Wood

VIII

From her perch at the top of the alder where Gytha had given birth, a female cuckoo looked out over the millpond. For three days she had kept vigil over a pair of reed warblers that nested among the reeds. While the hen warbler had been collecting flowering meadow grass to build her nest and carrying it back to the reeds, her mate had been in constant attendance. Therefore the sharp-eyed gowk, as some Gloucestershire folk once called the cuckoo, soon got to know where the nest was located and where she might lay another egg.

Throughout the latter half of May she had observed the comings and goings of other reed warblers that had returned to this same quarter of the valley, where reedy pond and stream were a haven for the birds. This same cuckoo had been raised the previous summer by a pair of reed warblers that nested on the same pond. The parasitic bird had inherited from its parents an instinct for seeking out other birds of the same species that would rear its young.

Soon after the female cuckoo had arrived in the valley, at the time the cuckoo flower, or lady's smock, began to bloom in the marshy ground alongside the stream in Shortcombe, her instinct to mate with sweet-singing males and to seek out the nests of reed warblers was awakened. Other cuckoos that had arrived even earlier had laid their eggs in the nests of dunnock, willow warbler and ruddock throughout the parish. So far did the cuckoo roam, and so secretive were its habits, that not even the young naturalists had been witness to its peculiar preying habits, though they had once found a dunnock's nest containing its mimicking egg along the railway embankment.

The hen cuckoo, accompanied by one of her mates, flew down from her high perch, uttering her water-bubbling chuckle. The cock bird made straight for the reed warblers' nest, while the hen waited her chance, perched on a low branch overhanging the millpond. Suddenly, amidst a flurry of wings, the warblers chased the cock from the reeds, and some distance away in another patch of reed, the angry pair scolded him as he clung to a swaying alder branch, balancing himself with his long tail. His innate intent was to lure the warblers from their nest for long enough to enable his mate to lay her egg. She had chosen to deposit it in a nest suspended on four reed stems, for she knew that this would give greater security to her large and clumsy offspring than would those nests supported by fewer stems.

While the warblers continued to mob the cock cuckoo, the hen laid her egg in the deep nest cup, then picking up the most re- cently laid of the warblers' two blotched eggs in her bill, she flew out of the reeds and across Shortcombe meadow in the company of her two consorts. A magpie watched from a hawthorn in which its nest lay hidden by leafy, blossoming branches, and a carrion crow flying over the pond saw the warblers return to their nest. But neither of the keen-eyed crows noticed the royal hunter carry off a young moorhen to its den beneath the roots of an alder.

A third of a mile to the west, at the edge of Dark Wood, the young stoats slept soundly beneath the roots of an old beech stump, for Gytha had recently moved them from their nest in the pollard willow. Now she needed to hunt more often to ensure that she caught sufficient prey to satisfy her kittens' healthy appetites. From sunrise to dusk she made quests of meadow, hedgerow, wood and warren for voles, birds and rabbits. Even during the small hours she would leave them to search the shady wood, often within earshot of badger and brown owl. Now that she brought them more meat, she suckled them less each day, so that some of her teats had begun to shrink. Despite the exertion of caring for her young, she seemed to have found new strength and courage in her pursuit of prey.

She stood in the shadow of the drystone wall, with one forepaw raised and flexed at the wrist. She lifted her muzzle into the mild southerly breeze that blew over the warren, carrying with it the scent of rabbit. A doe, in her second year, crouched low in the grass at the edge of the wood. Her superior senses were sharpened to detect the minutest movement and faintest scent of winged- and four-footed hunters. The doe, whose kittens lay nearby in a blocked stop, now bore five more young in her belly. They had been conceived the day after she had given birth to her second litter of the year.

The early evening sun was beginning to lose its former power. The warm earth radiated the doe's scent into the cooling air, so that Gytha's nostrils guided her to within sight of the rabbit. She saw the slim head, with ears erect, appear above a large tussock. For several moments she stood still. Then, with one light bound, she took cover in some nettles and sat low on her haunches, peering out to test the wind. The doe lowered her head again and nibbled the grass. Her ears were now laid flat along her back, though still perceptive to those waves of vibrant air that signal danger. As she bit off still more of the lush grass, the whole of her body was sensitive to alien tremors felt through the ground. Centuries of being the quarry of fox and stoat had instilled in the rabbit a need always to be vigilant, even in the dark depths of the warren.

Further whiffs of wind wafted more scent to the place where Gytha lay in wait, but she sensed that other, more easy, prey was to be found. She left the doe grazing the short, tender turf that generations of rabbits had made fertile and began to search the brambles at the edge of the wood. Soon she came upon the well-trodden entrance to a stop that held four two-week-old rabbits. Digging frantically with her forepaws, she enlarged the hole in the earth plug, which the doe had left to ventilate the nest, and cautiously ventured down the burrow.

The scent of the young rabbits filled the warm, humid nest chamber and excited Gytha more and more at each quick breath she took. She felt around in the darkness with her whiskered muzzle. The baby rabbits burrowed deeper into the thick bed of fur and dried grass. After four brief struggles all of them lay still. Gytha's canines had pierced each soft skull, entering the brain and killing the animal instantly. She hurried to the mouth of the burrow with one of the babies in her jaws, and without stopping to look around, emerged from the brambles and took the shortest route to her den.

She had hardly reached the drystone wall, when behind her she heard the pounding steps of another animal, and glancing round between bounds she caught sight of her pursuer. Seeing the doe rabbit, fur ruffled and furious, several lengths behind, made her hair bristle and her heart race even faster. The distressed doe was now so close that she could see the anger in its bloodshot eyes, which only a short while before had looked out timidly over the warren.

Although Gytha had made no sound during the plunder of the rabbits' nest, the doe had been alerted by the chacker of an observant magpie sitting in a thorn tree overlooking the warren. Now Gytha could hear the doe's threatening grunts and smell its rank breath as the distraught animal overtook her. The doe leapt in front of her, dug its front feet into the ground and struck out with its hindfeet, flinging her into the air.

Gytha landed on her back, and for a brief moment lay dazed

and winded. Her right flank ached where the rabbit had kicked her, but soon she was up on all fours again and bounding towards the spot where she had dropped her prey. She watched the doe hop back towards the brambles, and picking up the dead baby rabbit, which was about half her weight, she ran to her most recent nest beneath the old beech stump.

Before she had reached the end of the short burrow, several of the kittens tumbled from the nest in their eagerness to greet her. She let go of the rabbit for a moment, raised one forepaw and hissed angrily at the three kittens that blocked her way. Immediately they withdrew into the nest and waited expectantly until she brought her prey to the usual feeding place. All seven kittens surrounded the kill, sniffing it and burying their noses in the soft fur. The firstborn and one of his sisters licked the blood that had congealed around the small puncture wounds at the base of the rabbit's skull. Gytha turned the rabbit over on to its back and bit into the still warm belly. With her canines she tore the tender skin and muscle to expose the entrails, for she knew that here was food that her young would relish. She sliced open the rabbit's stomach to expose the white wad of clotted milk that had formed there after the suckling had taken its last feed an hour before.

Gytha had discovered the milk-filled stomachs of rabbit kittens in early spring, when she had eaten the solid milk to nourish her unborn young. She uttered a deep-throated trilling sound to tell her kittens to eat the nutritious food, though there was barely a mouthful for each. Then they began to eat the empty stomach and the rest of the gut. Two kittens found the succulent liver and bit pieces out of the blood-gorged organ, bolting them so quickly that they almost choked. The other kittens soon smelled out the bloody remains and eagerly lapped them up. In a short while they had eaten the heart, lungs, kidneys and rib cage, and then began to bite their way into the trunk and limbs, tearing off chunks of muscle and crunching the young bones between their milk teeth.

All seven kittens had now got their second set of incisor teeth in the upper jaws, and in the firstborn dog and the three bitches these had started to erupt in the lower jaws. The permanent teeth were thick, blunt and white, unlike the thinner, sharp and dull deciduous milk teeth. Now all the kittens had their eyes open they could discern daylight at the end of the burrow, yet they had no urge to leave the security of the nest. All had developed dark spots on the tips of their muzzles, and black hairs had begun to appear at the ends of their tails.

Gytha retired to one corner of the nest. She listened to the kittens champing on the remains of the rabbit's carcass and squabbling over the last morsels. She licked the bloodstains from her white forepaws and rubbed them over the sides of her muzzle. Her side still ached where the doe rabbit's hindfeet had struck her. As she massaged her bruised muscles with her tongue she felt the smallest bitch tug at one of her teats, and she turned to lick the sleepy face.

Like those of her littermates, the kitten's muzzle was now less blunt, and her head was beginning to lose its former bulbous shape. The muscles that covered the skull and supplied the jaws were growing stronger each time she used them to tackle the prey that Gytha brought back to the nest. But still the kitten found sustenance and comfort from sucking her teats. Only a few of the dozing kittens felt the touch of Gytha's tail tassel as she left them to fetch more of the baby rabbits.

Apart from the royal hunter, there were other creatures in Dark Wood that had to toil throughout the day to feed their offspring. High in the beeches a pair of willow warblers hunted for moth caterpillars, which included those of the winter moth. Since dawn the warblers had been searching for its soft-bodied larvae, which during daylight hours defied detection by mimicking twigs or leaf stalks. Yet many still fell prey to the keen-eyed warblers. During the night the caterpillars looped their way through the branches, gorging themselves on the tender young leaves, safe from the beaks of warblers, titmice and other small birds that reared their young in and around the wood.

The previous winter the wingless female moth had crawled up the tree trunk and laid her eggs singly in crevices in the bark. There the eggs survived frost, icy winds and rain, and when spring came they hatched. As the larvae grew fat in May they became prey for insectivorous birds, for Nature ensured that there was an abundance at the time they hatched off their clutches.

Racing along the edge of the wood, Gytha disturbed a bumblebee that had just alighted on her path. She paused to watch it crawl on to a bramble shoot, rest awhile, then fly off, its wings making a low, whispering drone, unlike the heavy hum of other bumblebees of its size. The female cuckoo bee had emerged from her winter quarters some time after the buff-tailed bumblebee whose nest she sought. She circled round the entrance to an old wood mouse nest in which the queen bumblebee had raised her first brood of workers. The cuckoo bee crawled down the tunnel that led to the nest chamber, attracted by the queen's scent. She felt around in the darkness with her antennae and found the queen straddling one of the waxen vase-like cells in which she was about to lay an egg.

Lying on her back, the queen struggled to fend off the attacks of the cuckoo bee, whose body was so strongly armoured that she could not inject her sting. But the impostor buried her sting between the shiny black plates of the queen's body and pumped in her poison. The queen lay paralysed and dying. With her loss, the workers would come under the spell of the cuckoo bee, whose eggs they would instinctively tend. The grubs that hatched from them would grow to become other cuckoo bees, and the females of these would in turn seek out the nests of the same kind of bumblebee the following year.

As Gytha entered the brambles she smelled the fresh scent of the doe rabbit whose young she had recently killed. Finding her babies dead, the doe had deserted the nest and now sat pining a short distance away, though near enough to catch the scent of the royal hunter. Gytha came out of the burrow with another baby rabbit in her jaws to see the doe standing nearby moaning and stamping her hindfeet on the ground.

Despite her recent encounter, Gytha remained cool and courageous, and carried off her prey into the wood. A short distance behind her followed the doe, still moaning and occasionally stopping to thump the ground. Gytha's pace seemed unhurried, and she had to make little effort to keep ahead of the rabbit. Along the ride in front of her she saw a cock pheasant. The old ringneck had just caught a vole, which he had killed with one stab of his powerful bill. He was about to swallow the rodent head first when he caught sight of Gytha, and picking up his prey and giving a short honk of alarm, he strutted proudly along the ride.

Higher up in the wood a figure watched the strange procession coming along the ride. The woodman had been alerted by the call of a startled blackbird, and had stopped his work to watch out for the royal hunter. Instead, he first saw the pheasant carrying the vole, and was amused by the bird's comical gait, for after a regular succession of steps it would give a little jump in the air. Next, he saw the beautiful royal hunter with her quarry, and he guessed she was living somewhere in the wood. Lastly, close on the stoat's heels, came the doe rabbit bemoaning the fate of her young ones.

Gytha approached the secret place where her kittens were concealed, and was about to turn off the ride into the undergrowth when the doe leapt in front of her and drummed loudly on the ground with her hindfeet. Gytha felt the ground reverberate beneath her and she dropped her prey in fright. The thought of being bowled over again by the angry doe was too much for her, and she rushed into the brambles. The doe sniffed at her dead one for a moment, and then turned about and bounded back along the ride.

Sensing the rabbit had gone, Gytha came out of cover and

ran over to the spot where she had dropped the dead one. The woodman, watching from behind a broad beech bole, saw Gytha pick up her prey and run off, and he now had a good idea where the royal hunter had her litter laid up. He remembered how, the previous year, a royal hunter with young in a tree hollow had spat at him while he was working in the wood. Gytha, hidden from the woodman's view, arrived at her den and pulled the young rabbit down into her nest beneath the roots of the old beech stump.

With even more daring she retrieved the last of the baby rabbits she had killed and carried it to a rabbit hole beneath the drystone wall, a short distance from her nest. She had taken the other two to her kittens, who now slept on full stomachs. She herself was ravenous after her hunt, and she bolted down the rabbit in the solitude of the burrow. When she had eaten she bent her head down between her hindlegs and licked herself clean. Her swollen genitals now stood out pink and moist, for her body was going through the changes that would prepare her to receive a mate.

On the way back to her kittens she stopped to sniff at a tuft of grass that bore the scent of another stoat, for a yearling dog stoat had passed the same way while she had been feasting and had left his scent mark. She sat up and looked back along the path she had taken, then ran a few steps and squatted down to leave behind her own peculiar scent that excited the senses of roaming dog stoats. Since coming into season she marked her ground more frequently, and over the past week the wind had carried her scent beyond the limits of her domain. Besides Aethelwald, there were yearling and older dog stoats whose keen noses were attracted to the strong scent of receptive bitches.

A carrion crow flying across the millpond spied a yearling dog stoat come out from under an alder, his belly full of young moorhen. For most of the day the crow and its mate had quartered their patch, seeking out nestlings on which to feed their fledglings. Out in Shortcombe meadow, a magpie inclined its head skywards as the great black crow passed overhead and, chackering, it flew to join its mate and their three surviving young. Since the gore crow had taken two of the magpies' nestlings to feed its own young, the lesser crow had become even more wary of its canny cousin.

Aethelwald travelled along the stream above Shortcombe, following closely the path taken by other dog stoats. He crossed Watery Lane at the same spot they had gone and ran into the blackthorn thicket at the corner of Oxlease. Swallows, which now had their young in the red-brick barn, skimmed and wheeled over the meadow, snatching up flies that cavorted around the cows, just back from the afternoon milking.

Among the dense hazel foliage, speckle-breasted ruddocks sat silently listening to their parents scolding the royal hunter as he made his way towards Dark Wood. The hen willow warbler, her bill crammed with tiny bright green caterpillars, waited awhile before flying down to her nest. An old buck rabbit saw the flash of the stoat's white throat amongst the thorny stems and lolloped off back to his burrow. All the way to the wood, ox-eye, blue tit and jenny wren revealed the stoat's progress by their alarm calls, and a few timid rabbits scuttled into their holes. Aethelwald stopped and smelled the places in the grass where Gytha had squatted, and where other dog stoats had left their marks. A humble-bee droned low over the grass, now and then settling to lick the moisture that contained vital minerals washed from rabbits' latrines by the previous night's rain.

From his roost high up in an ivy-bound ash, safe from foxes, the ring-necked pheasant listened to the stoats calling to one another in the dusk. Aethelwald had enticed Gytha away from her young with his seductive trilling, and she answered with her own crooning courtship call. The sounds the royal hunters exchanged with one another not only enabled them to make contact, but also served to heighten their sexual drives. Rarely has any human witnessed the nuptial of the royal hunter, for it is as secret as the courtship of the coney in its burrow.

In Dark Wood, alongside the drystone wall, Aethelwald and

Gytha chased each other through the undergrowth. Every so often Gytha stopped in her tracks and Aethelwald approached her cautiously, rubbing his underside over the ground with twisting movements and making excited trilling sounds. The pair sniffed at each other's hindquarters, calling incessantly. Then Gytha began to prance playfully around Aethelwald, who, aroused by her scent and sounds, grabbed her by the scruff of the neck with his teeth, as swiftly as he might pounce on a rabbit. With his powerful forelegs embracing her chest, he clasped her firmly and tried to mount her, but despite her playful advances, she was not yet ready for him. Several times she struggled and broke away from his grip around her waist, but she could not escape from his hold on her scruff.

The dozing cock pheasant at his tree roost heard the sounds of the courting couple as Aethelwald dragged Gytha around through the leaf litter beneath the drystone wall. Through two hourly chimes of the church clock, the pair lay coupled on their sides. When Gytha broke away from her sleeping sire, she tried to rouse him to further activity by dancing round him as she had done at the beginning of the nuptial. But he was too exhausted and oblivious to her amorous advances, and as dusk turned into night he remained curled up under an ivy-covered beech stump.

Gytha returned to her kittens, and after suckling them for a short while and grooming her ruffled fur, she too fell asleep. Soon her belly would bear the germs of new lives. But Nature had ensured that she would not be burdened with another litter until the following spring. Her kittens were still dependent on her, and for some time yet they would need to learn how to become true royal hunters.

Red-brick barn in Oxlease

IX

A male orange tip butterfly fluttered along Watery Lane, the orange patches on its forewings flashing like tiny beacons against the white lacy umbels of cow parsley growing tall by the hedge. Cuckoo pint, with shrivelled spathe and spadix, skulked in the hedge bottom against trailing ivy and goosegrass. In many of its flowers the lower part of the spadix was now girdled with young green fruits. The tiny flies that had pollinated the plant's peculiar flowers had helped to fatten and feather the young wrens in the stone barn.

Further along the lane, close by the hedge, grew garlic mustard, or Jack-by-the-hedge, known also as Jack-in-the-bush. On one of the flower heads a butterfly settled unseen, for the female orange tip lacked the alluring orange wing flashes of her mate. She held her wings partly closed, so that their mottled green undersides blended with the garlic mustard's white flowers and green stalks, as they also did when the insect sipped nectar from the cow parsley flowers. Hanging from the garlic mustard, she bent her body upwards and laid her eggs beneath the stalk of an unopened bloom near the tip of the shoot. By sticking each white egg to the young flower she ensured that when it hatched the larva would have a ready supply of the tenderest foliage to feed on. The same garlic-flavoured herb, known also as sauce alone, was once gathered by country people for its culinary and medicinal virtues. From the leaves and succulent stalks they made a sauce with which to garnish saltfish dishes, and from its boiled juices, mixed with honey, they prepared a cough cure.

Nearby, creeping over the hedge bottom, grew another herb that was once known by names as numerous and varied as the ailments it was said to cure. For centuries the ground ivy had been known in different parts of the wold as cat's foot, haymaids, turnhoof and Gill-go-by-ground, and it was picked for curing griping pains and choleric humours in belly and spleen, or gout in hip, hands and feet. The lowly herb was a member of the thyme family, whose conspicuous mauve flowers grew in whorls at the base of the hoof-shaped, purplish and pungent-smelling leaves. Once used for flavouring and clearing country-brewed beer, this hedgerow herb had been given the name of alehoof. In the hundred of Longtree, as in other parts of Gloucestershire, the ground ivy sometimes went by the name of 'run away Jack and Jill', on account of its habit of quickly spreading over the ground.

Long before the lane was covered with tarred stone, it was laid with local limestone, first broken with hammers wielded by men, then trodden by the heavy hooves of working horses and rutted by wooden-wheeled wagons. Wool-laden packhorses and drovers with their livestock once used this ancient way between Bath and Gloucester, which cut across the hillside from the northern end of Woodchester to the high common of Selsley in the north-west. The lane was first dug out of the clay, sand and limestone, and on the banks that were thrown up on either side a hedgerow had grown. In it were to be found hazel, hawthorn, blackthorn and ash, field maple, sycamore and elm, wayfaring tree, dogwood and elder. Some of the trees making up the old hedge men had planted, others had seeded from nearby woods, and still others berry-eating birds had accidentally sown. Over the ages the hedge had flourished under the skilful eye and hand of woodman and hedger, whether they be Celt, Roman, Saxon, medieval or modern. Within and around it wild rose, traveller's joy, bramble and ivy each found a niche, while a host of lesser herbs flowered and fruited in their own favoured sunlit or shady spot along the length of the lane.

In one of the sunnier aspects on the west bank, the bright pink flowers of herb robert shone out from the lush greens of grass and foliage. Over the ages this slender-stemmed herb, which may have been named after a French monk versed in the art of herbal medicine, had gathered such names as poor robin, Jenny wren, robin red shanks, dragon's blood and little bachelor's buttons. In the county of Gloucester the plant with the delicate ferny leaves had become known as red robin on account of its thin, ruddy, jointed stems. Herbalists once found a use for its strong-smelling juices in healing gangrenous wounds, stemming blood, and allaying stones in the kidneys. Farmers too were conversant with the healing herb, for they used it to treat their diseased cattle.

Still higher up the lane, on the high, moist bank, the tall stems of red campion showed off their rose-pink blooms against the rich green background of nettle and bramble. In some parts of the wold, the red campion went by names as varied as butcher's cow and Billy button, and because to the casual eye the flowers appeared as a larger version of herb robert's blooms, they came to be known as bachelor's buttons.

Another egg-laden female orange tip flew across the lane and vanished into a stand of cow parsley. The butterfly alighted on one of the frail flowers, closed her wings until they became part of the lacy umbel, and sipped nectar to regain her strength.

Growing among the grass at the bottom of a well-worn badger path the diminutive germander speedwell advertised its azure flowers. The speedwell was known in these parts as bird's eye, perhaps because of its resemblance to a jackdaw's eye. No other flower could match it for such clarity and depth of colour, and no passer-by could fail to notice it glaring up out of the grass. The petals were marked with fine lines of darker blue, which led tiny black, pollen-carrying flies to the centre of the flower where the nectar lay. As each flower became pollinated it lost its former brilliance, and closing against the fading petals, the calyx forced them off, so ensuring no other insect would waste its time searching for nectar.

Close by the speedwell, half hidden in the grass, grew the yellow archangel. A near relative of the white deadnettle, and relict of the damp woodland that once grew there, the archangel's flowers were favoured by bumblebees, whose eyes were lured by the rich yellow, red-streaked lip. Some country folk dubbed this flower weasel snout, since to someone's imaginative eye it seemed to bear a likeness to a weasel poking its muzzle out of the grass. Like its deadnettle relatives, the yellow archangel is still in flower on the twenty-ninth of September, the day dedicated to the Archangel Michael. It is also said to have shared with them a reputation as a guardian against evil spirits and spells, and for protecting cattle against a black magic disease called elf-shot.

At the top of the hedge bank the stems of white bryony had sprung from the soil and straggled over the hedge like a vine. The plant that was once so popular with medieval wood carvers and masons was better known as wood vine. When hedgerows became established features of the landscape it became known as the hedge vine. The climber used the hedge for support and to enable it to attain its full stature, in the same way that it depended on mature woodland trees. So rapidly did the bryony put out new shoots that scholars of botany named it after a Greek word that described this same herbaceous habit. By means of its grasping tendrils it gained a hold on the hedge and lifted its rich green leaves to the sun. The spiralling tip of the tendril curled round a leaf stalk or twig until it had a firm grip, and then it coiled up like a spring along its length, so pulling the stem closer to its support and gently anchoring it. So constantly and imperceptibly did the tendril tip gyrate that it was one of Nature's timepieces.

On the same bank lay a mesh of last year's dead bramble stems covering a small pile of old hedge trimmings, beneath which, in a hollow, a wren had built its nest. Some of the feathers that lined the nest were strewn over the bank among the thorny stems, and some lay on the lane below. The feathers, of cock pheasant and culver, had been pulled from the nest by a weasel as it had carried off the eight nestlings early that morning.

A few yards down the lane the vegetation around the stone water trough now grew even more luxuriant. The iron pipe that carried the spring water into the trough was hidden by the foliage of ivy and herb robert. The wood avens, with its small, deep yellow flowers, also preferred this damp and shady quarter of the lane. Over the years the wood avens had proved to be such a beneficial herb that monks, doctors of physic and ordinary country folk had called it herb bennet, for its magical powers seemed to have been derived from an association with St Benedict, founder of the Benedictine order of monks. Besides providing a potent cure for bodily ailments, the herb was said to have power over things spiritual, for its sweet-smelling roots were once hung about the house to protect its occupants against the devil.

Where the bank rose steeply, and seeping spring water kept it constantly damp, clusters of hart's tongue fern grew, the light green fronds, so aptly named, shining smooth and wax-like. In this same spot the moisture-loving fern had grown since this part of the lane had been dug out of the hillside. Distant ancestors of the fern grew in Coal Age forests many millions of years ago, and had become fossil fuel that men living at the time of the Roman villa mined in the Forest of Dean.

Close to the spot where the stream flowed underneath the lane, the woody-stemmed bittersweet rambled over other herbs and climbed clumsily over the hedge. Known also as woody nightshade, the herb was a feeble climber compared to the bryony and blithytwine. Of all the woodland and hedgerow climbers observed by that great naturalist and exponent of evolution, Charles Darwin, the bittersweet seemed to him the most ineffectual. For those concerned with herbal lore, however, the plant had many virtues. Hung around the neck, it dispelled witchcraft from the body of man and beast alike. Infused over a fire for twelve hours with white wine, a pound of the leaves and bruised stems made a potion that purged the body gently, healed bruises, helped dropsy and jaundice, and relieved those short of breath. Someone who bit into the stem found it tasted both bitter and sweet, and so the herb became appropriately named.

Of all the herbs of the hedgerow, none had ever been more widely sought after by country folk than the elder. Planted originally to strengthen fences against livestock and hold banks of ditches and watercourses, the elder tree was once an important source of dyes, salves, potions and beverages. The boiled bark gave black, the leaves green, and the berries blue, indigo and violet dyes. Its inner bark and root produced a powerful purgative and the leaves a more gentle purgative tea as well as a soothing ointment. The juice of the berries was taken both as a laxative and diuretic, but, fermented with honey or sugar, was more pleasantly imbibed as a poor man's port wine. The flowers were even in greater demand for preparing a lotion that was said to cure ulcers and sores of the skin, a syrup for coughs and colds, and a cosmetic water for the complexion. But then, as now, the heady blooms were most popular for brewing champagne and wine and for making herbal tea.

The elder grew at intervals all along the lane, the flat-topped clusters of creamy flowers effusing their singular spicy scent into the warm June air. One tree, which stood opposite the red-brick barn, had recently been divested of some of its flowers by Lilian Cashmore from Larchgrove Cottage, who each year made elderflower champagne and wine for maturing. The same tree had also been cut by the young naturalists and other boys from the village for its pith-filled stems, from which they fashioned popguns and pipes, as country children had done down the ages.

Away from the cool of the lane the meadows on either side glowed golden yellow in the heat of the day. The sun-glaring petals of meadow buttercup dazzled the eyes of two young girls as they walked through Shortcombe, the yellow pollen gilding their black patent leather shoes. The plant grew in such profusion because its acrid sap protected it from the discerning tongues of cattle. The same glossy petals attracted the subtler senses of insects, luring flies, beetles and bees to their bounty of nectar and pollen. In one buttercup bloom a small, orange, furry bee crawled with purpose over the pollen-yielding anthers, and with her legs combed off the yellow pollen that adhered to her body on to the brush of golden hairs beneath her belly. The female mason bee sucked up some nectar and flew to another flower to gather more pollen. Then, after climbing and circling skywards with sun-sensitive eyes, she made straight for the red-brick barn, where she settled on the wall in the full force of the sun.

The soft, limy mortar between the bricks bore many tiny tunnels that had been excavated from nooks and crannies by generations of solitary bees and wasps. The mason bee had emerged a week ago from one of these holes, in which her parent had nested the previous summer. The bee hesitated at the entrance, then scurried into the hole with her pollen load. The shaft, which she had enlarged with her sickle-shaped jaws, was no wider than her body, so that she was unable to turn round inside. At the end of the tunnel, some six times her own body length, she had built a back partition wall of mud. She had also fashioned a small crescent of mud around part of the tunnel's roof, a short distance from the partition, thus prescribing the limit of the first cell and ensuring that she would provision it with sufficient pollen for the needs of her offspring. Such a fascinating facet of bee behaviour had been discovered by that French father of entomology, Henri Fabre, who made a close study of solitary bees and wasps.

When the mason bee reached the pollen load she had delivered only a few minutes before, she regurgitated nectar on to it and with her nimble jaws worked it into a dough. Now her belly appeared at the entrance. She emerged, turned round, rubbed her shiny black face with her forelegs, and backed into the shaft. Close up against the pile of sticky pollen she rubbed her hairy hindlegs together over the pollen brush and combed out the pollen grains that were packed between the golden hairs. The bee's black head, with searching antennae, appeared once more at the entrance, and she saw a brightly coloured insect that had settled on one of the bricks of the barn.

The ruby-tailed wasp, its belly shining in the sun with the fire of a Burmese ruby, and its head and thorax the hue of azurite and malachite, had been lurking near the nest holes, watching the occupants working, for most of the morning. A few days before the mason bee emerged from its silken cocoon, the jewelled cuckoo wasp had hatched from one of the holes in which its host had nested the previous summer, and like the cuckoo bird, it now sought a place to lay its own eggs. The cuckoo wasp waited its chance. Now advancing, now retreating, with hesitant, agitated steps and quivering antennae, it looked like some animated jewel. During the mason bee's three more forays for pollen, the cuckoo wasp danced around the sun-drenched bricks, keeping watch over the activities of the solitary bees and wasps that nested in the mortar. Now that the mason bee had reached the crescent of mud marker, her instinct told her she had provisioned her cell with enough pollen, and she laid her first egg on top of it.

At the streamside the mason bee settled in a hoof imprint. She scooped up a minute amount of mud with her jaws, and holding it against the underside of her belly, thrust forward between her legs, she shaped it into a pellet, adding more mud to it until it was the required size. Then she flew back to her nest, the pellet of mud held between her jaws and supported by her front legs. As she entered the tunnel she caught the cuckoo wasp unawares, and instinctively the predator rolled itself up into a ball. With the vulnerable underside of its head and thorax tucked beneath the concave underside of its thick-skinned tail, the wasp was no easy victim for the stinging bee. Over millions of years such races of wasp, with their own peculiar stealth and armoury, had hunted after solitary bees and wasps, whose eggs, larvae, pollen or insect provisions were food for their predatory offspring. The mason bee released the mud pellet she had brought back to begin sealing her first cell. She grabbed the relentless wasp by one leg, dragged it out of the tunnel, and flying off, dropped it over the meadow.

From a burrow in the hedge bank behind the barn a rabbit bolted and ran up the side of Oxlease, followed at intervals of several seconds by three more, all of which ran wildly along the track of the first. The mason bee crawled cautiously to the entrance of her burrow, paused to look around, and flew off to gather another load of mud. A sixth rabbit emerged from the burrow, hopping slowly, and lay down, dazed, its ears drooping and its eyes filled with terror. It lay on the grass, petrified, as Aethelwald came out of the same hole. He had been working the rabbit bury after his noonday rest, and had singled out a three-quarter grown buck below ground. He pranced round the rabbit and pounced on it, holding on to its neck with his canines until the dying animal keeled over. Then, while its heart still pumped, he used his incisors to bore and rend behind the rabbit's ear until he had gorged himself with blood. Death did not always come swiftly to prey of the royal hunter.

Some country folk believed that stoats preyed on rabbits in order to suck their blood, leaving the corpse when they had taken their fill. It was certainly not unusual to come across such victims with no other mark on them than a circular patch of bloody flesh, the size of a halfpenny piece, behind one ear.

Aethelwald started to drag his kill, two and a half times his own weight, towards Dark Wood, and in the time it took him to reach the drystone wall, the mason bee had brought back three more pellets to seal her cell. These she sculpted into an ever-decreasing spiral of mud, kept moist with her own saliva, leaving a small opening in the centre. So much did the bee's actions resemble those of the craftsman who worked with stone and mortar that she was aptly named the mason bee.

While the mason bee worked, the cuckoo wasp, undaunted by its former maltreatment, had returned to the wall of the barn to wait its opportunity to lay an egg in the nest of its host. As the golden-haired tail of the mason bee appeared at the entrance, the wasp became excited and backed away out of sight into another burrow in the mortar. No sooner had the bee left her nest to collect another load of mud than the wasp ran to the nest hole and scurried inside. Through the narrow gap in the mud partition it pushed its ruby tail and laid an egg on the pile of pollen, next to the egg of the mason bee. Nature had equipped the cuckoo wasp with the means of protruding its tail through a hole that was narrower than the mason bee's head, so enabling it to secrete its egg at the last moment before the bee sealed her cell. Before the bee returned, the wasp had flown off to seek out the nests of other unsuspecting hosts, hawking up and down the sunny side of the red-brick barn.

The mason bee landed at the entrance with another pellet of mud, with which she closed the hole in the cell partition, unaware that the wasp had laid an egg. Many more journeys she made to gather mud to build other cells and pollen to provision them. By the time the sun had gone down below Dark Wood she had plugged the entrance to her nest hole, tamping down the moist mud and smoothing it off with the pair of horns on the front of her face. In order to dupe other insect predators, she had left a small space between the mud wall sealing her last cell and that which formed the final entrance plug, so creating a false entrance, in the same way that Stone Age man tried to deceive would-be pillagers of his stone tumuli.

In a few days the wasp's egg would hatch, and within a week that of the mason bee. But not until a month had passed, when the bee's grub had eaten the pollen, would the wasp's grub start to eat alive the succulent body of its host. Then, after spinning its silk cocoon, the young wasp would wait until the following summer before emerging from its cell, along with the mason bees that had survived the depredations of the ruby-tailed wasp.

In Dark Wood a culver called to his mate, who fed milk to her second brood of squabs. Within the cool, shady wood and along its margins, more birds sang than in the hedgerows bordering Watery Lane. The cock willow warbler sang his well rehearsed song from the top of the same tree he had used since his mate began to build in the tussocky grass behind the red-brick barn. Blackbird, thrush and chaffinch advertised their domains by their songs, which exhibited different variations to those of the same birds living in other parts of Longtree, or even in other parts of the parish. Burly bumblebees wandered low over the herb layer of the wood, their humming amplified by the lofty beech trunks and arched canopy, like cathedral columns and vaulted roof echo the organ's deep diapason. In a nest hole halfway up a straight beech bole, a brood of squawking fledgling starlings opened their yellow mouths to take food from the returning parent. Two years before, a green woodpecker, or yaffel, excavated the hole in the rotten trunk for its own nest. Though the starling had chosen the old yaffel's nest to rear its young, it little knew that the narrow entrance and bare, branchless bole would be no deterrent against preying stoat and weasel.

Dark Wood Lane

X

Gytha licked the white throat of her firstborn as he lay belly up amongst his sleeping siblings. Several days after Aethelwald had last mated with her, Gytha had moved her kittens from the den under the old beech stump to a more spacious rabbit hole beneath the drystone wall that surrounded Dark Wood. She had chosen the new home because it faced east and so caught the first warm rays of the rising sun, and because the wall bordered on the nine-acre marshy meadow that was a haven for field voles. It was the same meadow to which her mother had brought her kittens the previous summer, and it was their first hunting ground together.

The movement of the firstborn in response to Gytha's caress gradually woke the other kittens. Some thrust out their lusty limbs in their first stretch of the day, pushing gently against their littermates. The firstborn hauled himself over one of his brothers and squatted momentarily, ears alert in the darkness of the burrow, and then he crawled out of the nest to void the excreta from his last meal. One by one, the other kittens followed, each adding their soft scats of fur and feather to the piles that had accumulated in one corner of the nest chamber. Several of the kittens nuzzled Gytha's teats in search of her milk, for although her body now made less, she was still able to secrete sufficient to satisfy them, and the act of suckling in itself was essential to strengthen the familial bond.

All the kittens now wore the handsome black tail tassel of the royal hunter. The firstborn had grown slightly larger than his three brothers and was much longer and stouter than his three sisters. He resembled his father Aethelwald at that age. The last-born was slight of build, like her mother had been at the time she had conceived the year before. Gytha's firstborn we will call Aethelbeorht, which in the language of Woodchester's Saxon settlers means 'noble and illustrious one'. The lastborn we will call Aella, meaning 'she who has beauty'.

Gytha crawled along the burrow to the entrance. She smelled the scent of wet grass which the rising sun dispelled into the warm air from crystal clear raindrops clinging to the leaf blades. During the night and early morning heavy rain had fallen, which made the springs gush from the ground, swelling the runnels in the meadow and turning cloudy the water in the stone drinking trough. Tiny beads of water settled on Gytha's lustrous coat as she made her way through the lush vegetation in search of voles, roused from their burrows by the first rays of the sun. No birds, not even a magpie, noticed her leave her den, and no creature heard the sounds the boisterous kittens made inside.

Aethelbeorht tussled with one of his brothers in make-believe fight, springing on to his back and gripping his neck with his strong, deep-rooted canines. The smaller male then rolled over on to his back in a submissive attitude, repeatedly snapping his jaws at Aethelbeorht and trying to push him away with all four paws. At this, Aethelbeorht stood over him and pretended to bite his throat. Then he rolled over on to his back and his brother became the aggressor. Aella held one of her sisters by the scruff of the neck and dragged her around the den, while the third female, in less playful mood, cried plaintively until her two brothers released their hold on her. The den became filled with the excited clucking and chirping of the romping stoats, and the air was strong with the scent from their musk glands.

Throughout their growth, the three females had been more precocious than their four brothers, for they had long been sexually mature and able to conceive. But Nature had ensured that they could not have young by their brothers, since these would not reach sexual maturity until the following spring. Even before the kittens' eyes had opened, their den in the pollard willow had been found by a yearling dog stoat before Aethelwald discovered it. The alluring scent of the yearling had excited the cooing females to submit to his advances, and so all three now carried the germs of new lives in their young wombs. But like Gytha, who had also conceived again, they would not be able to give birth until the next spring.

Aethelbeorht became restless. He grew tired of play-fighting and crawled away from the other kittens on sturdy limbs. He was fascinated by the light at the end of the burrow. With his muzzle following the scent trail of his mother, he crept along the burrow and sat up on his haunches outside the entrance. It was not the first time he had wandered off from his littermates when Gytha was away. When she was with them, she would pull him back into the burrow if he crept off, for she feared for his safety. The young dog's eyes were still not accustomed to the bright sunlight, and he didn't become aware of the maggotty pie watching him from the top of the drystone wall, until the bird's noisy chatter startled him, and he scuttled into the burrow, emitting pungent-smelling musk into the air.

Hidden away within a grassy vole run Gytha sought her prey. The lush growth of the meadow had always been a stronghold of the field vole. Even during the great Ice Age, before the first humans reached these islands, the field vole had been a favourite food of the royal hunter. And before the Ice Age, in warmer climes, the vole's ancestors populated the grasslands and were the prey of other flesh eaters.

With their insatiable appetite for succulent grass stems, the voles multiplied in such large numbers that in some years there were plagues of them. At such times, owl, hawk, stoat, weasel and fox took advantage of the increased bounty, but an influx of these predators seemed to do little to check the prodigious populations. With its blunt-nosed head, small eyes and ears, squat limbs and short tail, the field vole was perfectly fitted to a life below ground, and above in its grassy galleries. The teeth that grew in its stoutly built skull could reduce the tough fibres of grass and roots to pulp as well as those of an elephant could grind up the branches of a tree.

With her slim, pliant body and short limbs, the bitch stoat, unlike the stockier dog stoat, was well fitted to hunting along the voles' runs above ground, and also those below ground. She was equally at home here as she was scaling trees and bushes for the eggs and nestlings of birds, and stalking small rodents was often less tiring than hunting after rabbits. Also, the dense cover of herbage shielded the royal hunter from the eye of the hawk, for at this time of her life, when she had to spend more of the day hunting to feed her family, she was more vulnerable to attack from predators. Each time she went on a foray, she was careful not to cover the same ground too often for fear of harassing her quarry so much that it became more difficult to capture.

She paused to sniff at a tiny heap of fresh, moist droppings that a field vole had recently deposited in its run between the grass stems. The nursing female vole had sensed the nearness of the stoat and had returned to her nest. She sat closely over her litter of seven, who snuggled in the nest of finely shredded, dried grass beneath a fallen willow branch. She had foiled the royal hunter by crossing the scent trail of another vole, a territory-holding male and sire of her young.

A hen blackbird cried out to warn the three surviving young of her second brood as she spied the grey-backed sparrowhawk streak along the edge of Dark Wood with a hen chaffinch in its talons. Gytha heard the blackbird's shindy and that of other birds, and she thought of her kittens. Sometimes, when she heard the birds' warning cries, she would lie up for awhile until they subsided, or if she felt uneasy about her kittens' safety, she would return to them straightaway. She was familiar with all the alarm signals of every bird, and from them could tell whether a fox, cat, weasel or hawk was about, or even whether another stoat was in the vicinity.

The birds' calls gradually died away as the sparrowhawk disappeared into cover to pluck its still sentient prey, and Gytha resumed her hunt. She followed a surface run along which a nursing vole had carried her young that morning from their waterlogged nursery below ground to a dry place under a tussock. The vole's scent was now faint, but it was sufficient to lead Gytha to the nest. Before she had pushed her muzzle through the flimsy, still unfinished, nursery, she heard the squeal of the mother as she forsook her nest with a young one in her mouth.

On hearing the warning cries of another vole that had winded the stoat, the mother had earlier carried off two of her babies and hidden them below ground. Gytha killed the four remaining young and carried them together in her jaws. In a hollow at the base of a clump of rush she laid them, close to the place where a badger had scratched out a vole's nest. With the dried grass from the nest she cached her prey, and squatting down she scent-marked the spot.

Gytha was resolute in her quest to kill sufficient voles to satisfy the appetites of her young, and she started to hunt again. She also had to feed herself. While the sun drew moisture from the ground, and with it the scent of voles, she would hunt for the remainder of the morning. Often, in preference to adults, she would seek out young voles in their nests. Even though they were also hunted by fox, badger, weasel and owl, there were enough voles in this and other neighbouring fields to provide for the stoat family. Throughout the warm spring, sun and rain had made the young growth of meadow grasses and rushes more nutritious than for several years past, and so the voles grew fat and fertile.

Gytha halted in her tracks to listen to the shrill, squabbling sounds of two voles nearby in the maze formed by the nibbled grass stems. A nursing female had been confronted by a roaming male and was returning his amorous advances by attacking him. Stalking softly along a side branch of the main run, Gytha moved towards the sounds. There was silence. The voles had winded the royal hunter, but only the female with young had gone to ground. The male sat rigid in a paroxysm of fear from the scent of musk that wafted towards his tiny nostrils.

Gytha cast around for fresh scent of vole, for she no longer relied on her ears alone to locate her prey. As she turned a bend in the run, she saw in front of her a flurry of grey-brown fur as the vole, suddenly released from his trance, sped down a run into which her path led. Her arched spine recoiled like a spring, thrusting her forepaws after her quarry. The vole was on unfamiliar ground, and even though he passed close to a hole, he chose to run on. Along the meandering runway Gytha pursued him, once overshooting his line so that she had to stop and pick it up again from the scent of other voles that had bolted down their burrows. She arrived at the end of the trail, the vole's scent strong in her nostrils. The vole had gone to ground.

Gytha pushed her muzzle into the mouth of the burrow, but found it was too narrow to get her head through. She scratched at the entrance and made soft growling noises, but the vole was way beyond her grasp, secure beneath the dark loam of the meadow. She searched around the tussocks and soon found another entrance to the vole's burrow, but again it was too narrow for her. Winding the vole within, she once more tore at the turf and drummed her hindfeet on the ground. Huddled in his nest, the vole listened to the enraged hunter and smelled the breath that came along the burrow, yet he felt secure within his earthy fortress.

Sensing that she would not be able to bolt the vole, Gytha returned to her cache, for she remembered the exact place she had hidden the young voles she had killed earlier. She removed the covering of nest material with her forepaws and picked up the voles in her jaws. On her way back to the kittens she passed close to the nest of another vole whose young had gained a reprieve from the royal hunter. When she arrived back at the den, she found the kittens fighting over the remains of two young starlings. While she had been away, the yearling dog stoat had scaled the beech tree where the starlings had nested and had taken all six fledglings. After caching four of them in his own den, he took two to Gytha's, where he had ingratiated himself with the young stoats and once more served the three bitches.

Later that same morning, soon after the church clock struck eleven, Gytha again left the nursery, but this time she didn't go to hunt on her own. She stood outside the entrance and encouraged her kittens with soft crooning sounds. The first one to appear was Aethelbeorht, his alert, blackberry bright eyes watching Gytha's every movement and his whiskered muzzle scenting the warm air that reflected from the sunlit wall. His three brothers followed close on each other's tails, and behind them emerged Aella ahead of her two sisters. Checking that all kittens were together, and that it was safe to leave, Gytha led them off into the meadow, choosing a different route to the one she had taken on her last foray.

The kittens followed Gytha in close formation, nose to tail, Aethelbeorht and his brothers ahead of Aella and her sisters. As she went through the long grass, constantly giving her contact calls to the kittens and flagging her black-tipped tail, she would frequently stop to look back and wait for her young train to catch her up. The sight and smell of the luxuriant herbage all seemed so strange to the kittens' senses that they would stop and linger after every few faltering steps. Aella sniffed at the stem of a horsetail, whose primitive leaves, as rough as a cat's tongue, sprouted from the hollow stem like bottlebrush bristles. She stood still and watched a turquoise-blue spider descend by its gossamer thread from a marsh thistle. At the same time she heard the shrieks of quarrelsome shrews, the rush of air from swallows' wings, and the noise the spring water made as it bubbled out of the ground, where blue-blossomed bugle and pink-petalled ragged robin grew.

Gytha led her kittens along the edge of a runnel that carried the spring water towards Watery Lane. She stopped giving her contact 'curoo' calls and began to stalk slowly between the stems of meadowsweet and willowherb, listening out for other minute sounds that the kittens' ears were not yet accustomed to. The young stoats kept their noses to the ground, following Gytha's scent trail, till Aethelbeorht and two of his brothers caught sight of her black tail tip twitching among the stems, and they all stopped and bunched together. They heard a brief squeal as Gytha pounced on a vole that was basking in its form, and they ran to greet her. She dropped her kill in front of them and began to paw it, in the same way that a cat plays with a mouse.

The vole was only stunned and started to run, at which Gytha pounced on it again, holding the back of its neck loosely in her jaws. Once more she released it and watched as Aella and Aethelbeorht leapt on the seemingly lifeless form. Aethelbeorht was the first to bury his young white fangs into the back of the vole's neck. The hours of play-fighting with his siblings had been a prelude to this, his first act of killing. Aella also sniffed at the vole's limp body and licked up the tiny drops of blood that welled from its wounds, and both she and her brother began to tear it apart and eat it, fighting off the advances of the other kittens.

Gytha spent what was left of the morning searching the meadow for other voles that had been enticed from their underground refuges by the sunshine. Although the voles were plentiful, they often got wind of the royal hunter and her family. Therefore, not all the kittens became initiated in the art of killing their own prey. But the June day was still young, and Gytha knew that before the sun went down over the Severn, all her kittens would have tasted the warm blood of their prey, for she had plans to take them further afield to new hunting grounds.

Two young magpies, which had recently left the nest, gave

their flute-like calls from their unsteady perches as they watched Gytha and her young leave the old rabbit hole beneath an ash tree, where they had been sleeping off their meals of vole during the heat of the early afternoon. A pair of willow warblers too called out anxiously to their fledged young while they searched the foliage for caterpillars. As Gytha led her kittens along the hedgerow she kept an ever-watchful eye on them and chivvied any that lingered too far behind, for she was always mindful of the danger from other predators that used the same route.

The royal hunters reached the tumbledown drystone wall at the bottom of Dark Wood. Where it had been reduced to two feet in height, Gytha leapt up on to it and ran backwards and forwards along it, encouraging the young stoats to follow. They had not yet had occasion to climb tree or wall, and Gytha intended this to be their first lesson. Extending himself up against the wall, Aethelbeorht clawed the lichen-encrusted limestone with his forepaws and pulled himself up high enough to find a grip with his hindlegs. He climbed using the same alternate movements of opposite foreleg and hind limb that had been so natural to him when he had first crawled in the natal nest to find his mother's teats. The stone felt rough against his soft young pads, for up until now they had only trodden the earth of the den and the turf of the meadow. Once the claws of one forepaw slipped on the weathered limestone, but the fear he felt was short-lived, and he reached the top of the wall before any of his brothers and sisters had gained their first footholds.

Gytha became agitated as one of the kittens sat at the bottom of the wall, reluctant to climb it. Aethelbeorht and two of his brothers had scaled the wall and jumped down into the wood, leaving Aella and two of the other kittens looking from the top at their sister pining below. Gytha's encouraging calls were to no avail, and she sprang down on to the ground, and picking the kitten up by the scruff, she carried it over the wall into the wood, followed by the rest of her family.

The young stoats' journey through the wood was yet another

experience for them. Again, with Aethelbeorht taking the lead, they followed Gytha in an inverted 'V' formation, each holding its head raised above the hindquarters of the one in front in order to keep their mother in view. Down into a deep dell they careered, rolling over in their excitement and endeavour to keep up with her. At the bottom of the dell they hesitated as they encountered the unfamiliar musky scent of a dog fox, which had recently retired to his earth at the top of the wood. Their eager young noses lingered over the spot where the fox had left his mark, until they heard Gytha calling them from the top of the dell.

Up the steep side of the dell the young stoats scrambled, throwing their tongues like miniature hounds and making a kind of yaffling cry, like beagle puppies in playful pursuit of the bitch who refuses to allow them to catch her up. Now and then the troupe would stop to investigate some new strange smell that Gytha had discovered, or stand with ears pricked to listen to the call of a cock pheasant or the tinkle of contact calls made by a family of long-tailed tits hunting for caterpillars in the beeches.

When Gytha came to the drystone wall that enclosed the wood on its southern side, she gathered the kittens together and led them through a gap in its base into the grass verge at the side of Selsley Road. Because this upper stretch of the road cut through Dark Wood it was known locally as Dark Wood Lane. Pausing at the edge of the verge to check that all the kittens were with her and that the way was clear, she darted across the road, encouraging them to follow with soft clucking sounds and by whisking her tail. Lilian Cashmore, who was picking elderflowers by the roadside, noticed the stoats run across the road, and she thought how much they resembled a piece of brown rag being blown by a gust of wind.

No sooner had the kittens reached the opposite verge than Gytha dashed back across the road, calling out in alarm with loud, rapid clucking noises. One of the female kittens had not crossed over and was squatting, petrified, in the grass as a sparrowhawk swooped down on to it. In a fury Gytha raced to the kitten's rescue. Cackling loudly, she sprang at the female sparrowhawk and tried to grab it by the throat. But it was all she could do to dodge the repeated blows from its hooked bill, and she only managed to claw some feathers from its breast as it became airborne with the young stoat held tightly in its talons.

The kitten tried to turn its head to bite the hawk's legs, but the scimitar-sharp claws had paralysed its neck muscles. As they drew blood it ceased to struggle, and its body went limp as the hawk carried it off into the wood. Gytha, distraught by the loss of her young one, bounded back and forth across the road in agitation, making the sorts of sounds that only a mourning mother stoat makes, and at the same time calling out to reassure her kittens who were trembling with fear beneath the drystone wall on the opposite side of the road.

The Dingle

XI

On the south side of Dark Wood Lane, which Gytha and her six kittens had crossed the previous day, stood the continuation of Dark Wood. It was also known as Lily Wood on account of the lilies of the valley that grew there. Some say the name of the wood signified a burial place of local heroes who fought at the battles of Dyrham and Tewkesbury. Others say it was derived from 'Blacklow', the name given to the Saxon hundred of which Woodchester was once a part, and by which the Stone Age long barrow on Selsley Common was sometimes known. Formerly called Dog Wood, this portion of the wood covered the north side of another, larger combe and merged with woodland on its south side called Dingle Wood, because of the dingle on its northern edge. The wood had also once been called Withy Wood on account of the willows that used to grow along its wet lower slopes and whose pliant branches, or withies, had been harvested by basket weavers since Celtic times.

Below the woods hedgerowed fields sloped down to a stream, which issued as springs near the head of the combe where the two woods converged. The stream had cut a deep channel in the thick clay, and along its steep banks ash and alder grew. A few willows standing in marshy ground marked the site of a former pond, long since silted up and overgrown. From here the stream meandered through pastureland and finally flowed into a lower reedy pond, which once powered the millwheel of Southfield Mill. In more recent times it drove a turbine that generated electricity supplying Southfield Mill House. The stream was a watering place not only for cattle and sheep but for badger and fox, and the ponds were havens for waterfowl and warblers. The young naturalists knew this peaceful place as the Dingle, and the stream they called 'the dip' since sheep were once washed in it.

For centuries the Dingle had been a stronghold of the rabbit, which had burrowed deep into the Cotswold sand beneath its pastures and woods. The first rabbits to live in the parish were brought over after the Norman Conquest and were kept in man-made warrens. No one knows whether or not rabbits were kept on the Dingle's sunny southern slopes when the earls of Salisbury farmed the land, or when the Maltravers family held the land by knight service from the earls, or even when the first warrener was employed on the manor. But it is recorded that in 1360 the parson of neighbouring Stroud was entitled to tithes of rabbits, dove houses, fish ponds, fowling and hunting, along with a multitude of others, in return for curing souls, binding books, washing surplices, providing wax to light the church and wine for communion. At such a time the rector of Woodchester would have taken similar tithes and stored them in the large tithe barn that once stood in the rectory grounds.

On the north side of the Dingle lay a field which a century and a half before was known as Coneygre, a name signifying its former use as a rabbit warren. At that time, when Thomas, Earl of Ducie, was lord of the manor, a certain John Wintle rented this seven-acre field and also managed a withy bed by the stream. Several centuries before farmer Wintle tended his crops, some unknown warrener cared for his conies on this same seven acres.

The warrener would have built a drystone wall around the warren to deter rabbits from straying. But it didn't prevent some of them burrowing their way out, nor did it keep out predators and poachers.

The warrener would have been familiar with the habits of all feathered and furred hunters on the manorial estate, and he knew where to set his traps and snares. He observed that the buzzards and kites that flew over the warren would perch on the wall or on the earth mounds he had provided for the rabbits to burrow into. He therefore raised other piles of earth and stone, or drove stakes into the ground, and to these he anchored iron traps with toothed jaws. The same traps were used for the royal hunter, which he set in stone tunnels around the outside of the drystone wall. He also knew that no fox could resist the smell of a dead cat, so he would bury one he had caught beneath a trap.

The warrener of Woodchester had to use all his wit and craft in caring for conies. To ensure they were kept free from disease, he would kill any weak ones, especially when they began to breed and in the autumn, for he knew that a frail doe was more likely to have small litters and weakly kittens that would be more prone to disease and less likely to withstand wet weather. During the winter, when the grass on the warren was in short supply, he would feed his conies hay, greenstuff and root crops to ensure that those he ferreted were fat and healthy for the lord of the manor.

Whereas much of the warrener's work was a battle of wits between him and the predators and poachers, on occasions a warren became the scene of human conflict, and even the subject of royal litigation. It is recorded in 1626 that, as a result of certain riots and offences committed at a warren and its lodge in Woodchester and neighbouring King's Stanley, Charles I signed a Star Chamber commission to sequestrate the warren and all its properties. The warren was the property of the lord of the manor, William Huntley, and was the one that was now covered by that portion of Dark Wood on the north side of Dark Wood Lane where one of Gytha's kittens had fallen prey to the sparrowhawk.

At the edge of the wood, on a hillside sheep pasture known as Sunny Bank, which had been formed by clear-felling some of the area, Gytha and her kittens basked in the first rays of the rising sun at the entrance to a rabbit burrow that had been their shelter during the night. The young stoats were in playful mood, and Gytha no longer pined for the kitten she had lost the previous day. Aethelbeorht picked up a rabbit's paw, left over from their last meal, and ran round and round the hole, encouraging the others to take the plaything from his jaws. But he was more energetic and agile than his brothers and sisters, and they soon tired of the sport. While he raced round in ever-decreasing circles, occasionally challenged by one of his brothers, Aella and her surviving sister started to play a game of tag with the other two dogs, until they too lost interest and became fascinated by their mother's twitching tail tip.

Gytha had been sitting keeping a watchful eye over her kittens. She had also been watching the warren and noticed that there were more rabbits out feeding than was usual for the time of day. Rabbits were leaving their burrows, even on the windward side of the stoats, yet they grazed intently and unperturbed, like herds of wildebeest watched over by a pride of lions. Gytha looked on, bemused by the strange antics of the animals whose acute, primitive senses could detect the gathering storm.

Young rabbits of litters born from March to May frisked and raced about the warren, scattering others in their paths. Some leapt in the air, and simultaneously twisted or shook their bodies and kicked out their hindlegs, while others rolled on their backs with their legs in the air, like playful puppies. The whole warren seemed to be in a kind of frenzy. Then, gradually, their bizarre behaviour abated, and they settled down to graze. Each rabbit cropped the grass of the warren in a semicircle, casting its head from side to side, and after several sweeps it shuffled or hopped forward down the hillside to repeat the pattern. The sun's strengthening rays brought out even more rabbits to feed or frolic and stimulated those that had already filled their stomachs to bask or groom.

Gytha's gaze was suddenly directed towards an old buck rabbit who paraded around his patch, rubbing his chin on the ground and on the backs of does in his harem. This he had done so frequently that his fur had become matted with dirt and encrusted with the secretions of his scent glands. He also made his presence known to his subordinates by rubbing his chin over bramble stems, and by depositing his scented droppings at regular latrines over the warren. He was one of a select few dominant bucks who had survived several close encounters with Aethelwald.

Now most of the occupants of the warren had left their burrows, and rabbits whose lineage went back to the founders of Coneygre fed alongside those whose parentage was not so pure. The rabbits' superior senses, which gave such uncanny premonition of the impending storm, spurred them on to fill their bellies before the rains came. Creatures of comfort, they were more at home in the warmer climes of their countries of origin, and were rather intolerant of cold and damp. But the maze of burrows they had made in the cool, well-drained subsoil of the Dingle was testimony to their adaptability.

Now Gytha's attention was drawn to the plight of two young rabbits that ran towards her. Now and again they would stop in their tracks and then continue on their erratic paths, seemingly with ever-decreasing energy, for they were being pursued by a large dog stoat, which Gytha soon recognised as Aethelwald. The young stoats darted into their den, except for Aethelbeorht and one of his brothers, who stood behind their mother watching the hunt approach.

The old buck rabbit became agitated and thumped his hefty hindfeet on the ground, sending some of his harem and their offspring scurrying for their burrows. Aethelwald also felt the reverberations beneath the pads of his hindfeet as he stood and watched some of the warren's more timid tenants take refuge. He had also noticed the big buck rabbit standing sentry a few yards ahead. No sooner had he pounced on the young rabbit that had given up the chase than the buck rabbit thundered towards him, growling and grunting and making himself look even larger by raising his fur. Before the buck had cast his shadow over Aethelwald, the royal hunter released his hold on the rabbit and ran for the wood, with the buck in hot pursuit.

Standing on top of a beech stump, Aethelwald glowered back at the old buck, cackling with rage through bared teeth and brandishing his elegant brush, the long hairs of its black tag bristling. But the threat to Aethelwald was short-lived, and the buck turned tail and hopped back to join the young rabbit that had escaped its brother's fate. The rabbit Aethelwald had wounded lay kicking and squealing, and when the buck rabbit had returned with its surviving offspring to a burrow, he killed and carried his prey to the rabbit hole where Gytha and her family were lying up. Several times he had brought his kill to the stoats' den in order to ingratiate himself with Gytha and the young females, but unbeknown to him, his daughters had already conceived by mating with a stoat several years his junior.

Two other bitch stoats whose domains were also encompassed by that of Aethelwald had their young several weeks after Gytha had given birth, and as neither the mothers nor their offspring had yet come into season, they had not been discovered by Aethelwald or other dog stoats. It was not common knowledge that the old dog stoat had any part in raising his offspring. But then it was usually only woodmen and gamekeepers who ever chanced upon a stoat's nest, and rarely one with the whole family at home.

Straightaway Aethelwald began to hunt again, for the sight of so many rabbits feeding had unleashed the stoat's natural urge to kill repeatedly. It was an instinct that went back to the periods of the Ice Age when the land was under permanent snow. At such times a rare encounter with a plenitude of prey was seen as an opportunity for the stoat to lay up stores for leaner times and so conserve precious energy expended in hunting in a harsh climate.

Soon Aethelwald had singled out another unsuspecting rabbit, and was on the point of delivering the death blow when the old buck rabbit once more appeared on the scene. Squealing loudly, as if itself in terror of a royal hunter, the buck leapt over Aethelwald and made an about-turn in mid-air to confront him with pummelling paws. The prospect of being mauled by the buck's long slashing claws was too much for him, and abandoning his prey, he galloped up the Dingle as fast as his short legs would carry him, with the buck rabbit following close behind. He left Coneygre, and without looking back raced over an eight-acre field, which was once glebe land belonging to a past rector of the parish, the Reverend Doctor Williams, and ended up in a hummocky field called the Devil's Bowling Green, amidst a colony of surprised rabbits.

The old buck rabbit had long since given up the chase, and he loped back to Coneygre, leaving Aethelwald yet more determined to kill again. For his next attempt he adopted other, more unusual, tactics. He lay stretched out on his side, in the middle of the hummocky pasture, recovering his wind and eyeing a group of rabbits that sat up on their haunches watching him. Then he got up and bounded over towards them, following a zigzag course. It was not his usual gait, more the gambol of a spring lamb, for he threw his hindlegs out behind him and whipped his tail violently, and after every few seconds he would turn a somersault or roll over and over on his side. Several rabbits hopped towards him, fascinated by his frolics. Then he began to move in circles in front of the bemused spectators, twisting and tumbling and chasing his tail, all the while edging nearer and nearer to them.

Other rabbits joined those already transfixed by Aethelwald's capers. He continued to dash around in ever-widening circles, until he passed almost within springing distance of several rabbits, who crouched motionless, mesmerised by this strange behaviour. Suddenly, he stopped in mid-circuit and began to dance around on his hindlegs, with his forepaws held up like a begging dog. As he pranced past one unsuspecting rabbit, he turned in his tracks and leapt on its back, his jaws soon finding the vulnerable spot between the first two vertebrae of its skinny neck. Before the rabbit felt the stoat's fangs, its screams broke the bewilderment of the rest of the colony, and they rushed for their holes at the edge of Dark Wood, while Aethelwald gorged himself on the blood of his kill. Woodman and gamekeeper alike could vouch for the royal hunter's dance of death, but this time only the Dingle rabbits had witnessed the roguish ritual.

While the lightning flashed and the thunder rumbled over the vale, the rain fell in torrents. Rabbits from all over the Dingle were confined to their burrows, where they digested recent meals or re-ingested their soft, newly voided pellets from which they obtained valuable vitamins. Gytha and her young huddled together in their dry den, dozing through the thunderstorm after eating the rabbit Aethelwald had caught, while he slept among the straw of a stone barn that stood in a thirteen-acre pasture on the south side of the Dingle, known as Barn Field.

The barn was just one of many resting places he used on his domain, particularly in bad weather, for the royal hunter could not tolerate damp and draughty dens. He lay curled up in one corner of the barn, close to his last kill. Between his shoulder blades sheep ticks, with bald, bloated bodies resembling castor oil seeds, clung to his pelt and sucked his blood through their lancet-like jaws embedded deep in his skin. As he slept, the smaller male ticks crawled over his fur and impregnated the fat females. He was powerless to rid himself of the parasites, which he had picked up from sheep pasture.

The ticks were now in their third summer and nearing the end of their long life. Three springs past they had lain in wait, clinging to the tips of grass blades, and sensing the warm body of their host, be it sheep, fox or stoat, had crept into its coat and buried their mouthparts beneath its skin to suck its blood. During each summer they had grown fatter on the blood they had consumed at each brief repast, and throughout each autumn and winter they lay still and torpid beneath the grass stems, until the following spring when they chanced upon another host.

Aethelwald was also plagued by parasites unseen. Since the previous autumn, worms living inside the warm, wet bony passages of his skull had been feeding on the blood that bathed his brain, without causing him any apparent suffering. The large, egg-filled female worms and their smaller male partners occupied the sinus above his left eye, and had caused the sinus wall to grow deformed, so that it began to press on his brain. He had become infested with the parasitic worms by eating wood mice that harboured the same parasites in their heads. The wood mice themselves had become infested by eating woodland snails that glided over the scats of stoats and weasels containing the microscopic dormant larvae of the worms.

Each time Aethelwald had eaten an infested wood mouse the young worms wriggled free, bored through the gut wall and migrated along the spinal cord to the sinuses, where they grew to maturity. The female worms ensured the survival of the species by shedding their larvae into the fluid bathing the sinus, from where they swam down the back of the stoat's throat into the gut, to be released into the outside world each time he voided his scats. In the dewy grass the larvae would wait their opportunity to penetrate the soft, slimy sole of a snail, and so continue their hazardous life cycle.

While Aethelwald slept, oblivious of the insidious parasites inside his skull, a barn owl dozed under the roof tiles of the barn, unaware of the royal hunter sleeping in the straw below. Like the stoat, the barn owl had benefited from man's devastation of the forest, for it depended on marshy meadows and rough grassland for its prime prey, the field vole. Nevertheless, it also hunted wood mice, shrews and songbirds along the woodland edge and hedgerows, and killed many rats around the farms. But the barn owl was careful not to compete with the more aggressive tawny or wood owl which nested in Dingle Wood and Dark Wood. The more delicate barn owl, which found some of man's buildings substitutes for its more natural cave haunts of warmer climes, had suffered heavy losses during the recent harsh winter, when its hunting grounds had been snowbound for several months.

For the rest of the morning, while the rain still fell, Aethelwald slept soundly in his bed of straw, and the ever-vigilant owl stayed at its roost. At midday the rain finally ceased. Aethelwald woke, scratched behind his neck in a vain attempt to rid himself of the ticks, stretched, and ate some more of the rabbit. The minute sounds he made, whether rustle of straw or crack of bone, were reflected by the ruff of dense feathers surrounding the owl's white face through sparser, filamentous feathers covering the large ear conches, where they became perceptible noises. To the white-breasted owl such sounds were so familiar in the barn, for they were similar to those produced by the rats that lived there.

Aethelwald stole away from his shelter, unseen by the barn owl, and made his way down the side of Dingle Wood, keeping to the cover of the drystone wall. As he patrolled this quarter of his domain, he marked his trail by leaving his scented scats on pieces of limestone or fallen branches, or rubbing his hindquarters on them. He broke cover at the bottom of Barn Field, where it joined a field known as The Laggar, and followed one side of an old hazel-lined track called Laggar Lane. Some way along he ran down a hedgerow that bordered a seven-acre field, known as Bean Acre in Farmer Wintle's day, towards the alder-fringed stream.

The barn owl opened its eyes to glimpse a rat run across the barn floor, attracted by the smell of the rabbit's remains Aethelwald had left amongst the straw. A bulge appeared in the owl's throat. It lowered its head between its hunched wings, and opening its mandibles wide ejected a large smooth pellet of compacted fur and bone, which fell to the floor to join others that had accumulated there. The sudden removal of the pellet was a natural reaction to the sight of prey and desire for another meal. The owl waited, its head bobbing to left and right in order to focus its eyes and ears on the rat. As the rat appeared, carrying the mangled remains of the rabbit, the owl pounced from its roost. Wrapping its claws around the rat, it seized the muzzle with its hooked bill and jerked the head backwards to dislocate the neck. In the grip of one foot it carried the rat back to its roost where it bit off the head and swallowed it before consuming the rest of the animal.

Early the next morning, before sunrise, Aethelwald left another of his dens in a tree hollow and ran along the track by the brook, at the eastern edge of his domain. Since the willow warbler had arrived, the vegetation by the side of the brook grew dense and lush. Succulent-stemmed angelica and comfrey, yellow archangel, heady-scented meadowsweet and blue-flowered bugle each competed for growing space. Just before the stone bridge that crossed the brook, Aethelwald surprised an old buck rabbit who was feasting on the herbage. Both animals stood a yard apart, each up on its haunches glowering at each other like two boxers in a ring.

Aethelwald sprang for the rabbit's neck, but before he could fasten on to it, the crafty buck jumped nimbly sideways and braced itself for the next assault. Three more times Aethelwald tried to bury his canines in the rabbit's neck and three times his attacks were thwarted. A fourth time the rabbit side-stepped its assailant, and crossing the bridge, ran to the end of the track where it met the main road, with Aethelwald in close pursuit. So intent was he in getting his quarry that he neither saw nor heard the car come round the bend, nor did he feel any pain as its front wheel broke his broad back.

He lay limp in the gutter, blood trickling from his open mouth. A carrion crow alighted on the drystone wall at the far side of the road and watched the buck rabbit run along the side of the wall and escape under a gate into an orchard on the steep hillside. The black crow flew across the road and perched on the opposite wall. It lowered its head to eye the corpse, and after checking that the way was clear, flew down into the road and began to peck at the ticks that clung to the royal hunter's warm body.

St Loe's House

XII

The June sun beat down from a clear blue sky on to a grassy slope on the south side of Dingle Wood once known as Cock pits. For as long as anyone in Woodchester could remember, the pasture had never felt the bite of the ploughshare, neither had cattle grazed there as they did on the high commons. Seasonal flocks of sheep and the ever-present rabbit prevented the land reverting to the woodland of Domesday times and helped maintain the rich variety of flowers that grew among the grasses. Rabbits kept the grass short on the nest mounds of the yellow ant, so enabling the sun's rays to warm up its soil fortresses, and they also used the larger mounds as latrines.

The anthills were dotted over much of the sunny slope and each one was aligned east to west so as to receive the maximum benefit of the life-giving sun throughout most of the year. So constant was the ant in its habits that a lost traveller could use its mound as a compass, for the steeper, more rounded end always faced the east, and so received the first rays of the rising sun. Such a design was reminiscent of the Neolithic long barrow, which was also aligned with its steeper, broader end facing east.

Sweet-smelling wild thyme crept over the close-cropped turf of the anthills, and around the edges of some of them yellow rockrose and blue milkwort grew. The grass between the mounds was longer and spangled with the yellow and orange flowers of bird's-foot trefoil. Rabbits living in Dingle Wood made their runs through the grass and cut clearings of shorter turf by their constant grazing. These formed a lattice between the anthills and the islands of flowers and long grasses covering a stretch several yards out from the woodland edge. Where the grass covered a large mound of spoil from an old quarry, dating back to the days when limestone was dug there, rockrose grew alongside squat horseshoe vetch, mouse-eared hawkweed and the first magenta flowers of pyramidal orchid. During the winter snow the old quarry spoil was a popular sled run for the local children.

A multitude of butterflies flew about the flowery field, while others, under the disguise of their closed wings, rested, laid their eggs, or sipped nectar from thyme, trefoil and vetch. A male common blue flashed his lilac-blue wings at his dusky-winged mate as she settled on the bird's-foot trefoil to lay another egg. Around a thyme-covered mound another blue butterfly hovered. Its wings were larger, of a rich violet-blue colour, spotted and bordered with black. This was the rarest of all the blue butterflies and the one that collectors coveted above all others. Victorian lepidopterists had netted the large blue in its hundreds, when it was as plentiful as its lesser relatives. But rather than the zealousness or greed of some of these early naturalists, it was the butterfly's unusual life cycle and dependence on the Cotswolds' closely grazed slopes that made it such a rarity.

The female large blue that now settled on the mauve thyme flowers had emerged from her chrysalis only the previous day, and had just started to lay her eggs. She had begun her precarious existence the previous year as a minute larva that hatched from an egg inside a young thyme flower. For several weeks the larva fed on the thyme's pollen and fruits, and as it grew its colour and downy covering gave it a resemblance to the herb's flower buds. In this way it found protection from the eyes of predators as it crawled from flower to flower. The large blue larva was itself a predator, for it ate other large blue larvae that it came across, and it only ceased to be a cannibal after it had moulted its skin for the last time. It then dropped from the flower and lay hidden under the leaves, awaiting discovery by one of the red ants that often raided the nest of the yellow ant.

Soon a red ant had encountered the large blue larva and straightaway began to stroke it all over with its antennae, which made a gland on its body exude a sugary liquid. Several yellow ants, which had been carrying particles of soil to extend their nest mound, also stopped to investigate the larva, and they too caressed it, dropping their burdens to taste the sweet secretion. When the yellow ants had left the scene to aid their fellow workers in the defence of their nest against a party of marauding red ants, the solitary red ant still coaxed the larva to give up more of its sweetness. After an hour's courting by the ant, the larva swelled up its pallid, hairy body, which made the ant seize it in its jaws and carry it off to its nest.

Through the rabbit-cropped grass the ant ran with its prize, stopping frequently to share the tasty exudate with others of its own species. But the ant had no need to defend its claim on the larva, and resumed its journey unhindered. Following the scent trail left by foragers from its own nest, the ant arrived at the nest, which lay beneath a slab of sun-baked limestone, and down into the dark brood chamber it hauled the larva.

For the rest of the year the large blue larva lived underground as a host of the red ant, feasting on its grubs and hibernating as a bloated white grub that dwarfed the ants' larvae. As winter gave way to spring, the larva woke and began to feed again on the ants' grubs. Towards the end of May it reached full size and changed into a pupa, and after three weeks the large blue butterfly hatched, crawled along the ants' galleries and emerged into the outside world, where it inflated its beautiful blue wings in the late June sunshine.

Now another blue butterfly, the adonis blue, settled on the same patch of thyme covering the ants' mound, and sipped nectar alongside the egg-laying large blue. Though not quite so rare as its larger cousin, the adonis was still very much sought after by butterfly collectors, for few could resist the sight of the male's bright azure-blue wings. The wings of this male were worn and had lost their pristine brilliance, for the butterfly was nearing the end of his short life. Some females with which he had mated had laid their eggs on the horseshoe vetch that grew on the old quarry spoil, and from them had hatched larvae that fed on the plant's leaves and flowers. Like the larva of the large blue, that of the adonis yielded a sugary secretion that ants could not resist. The yellow ant, being the commonest ant on this sunny slope, hunted after the adonis larva, and in return for its sweet offerings protected its vulnerable soft body from predatory and parasitic insects.

In past years some blue butterflies had been captured on the high commons on the opposite side of the valley, not to be pinned out in cabinets, but to be used as living subjects for watercolour paintings. The artist, Edith Payne, widow of stained glass artist Henry Payne, lived at St Loe's, an old house that stood on the hillside below St Chloe, the site of the medieval manor of Seynckley. Both the names of the old house and the manor had their origins in Anglo-Saxon times, when there was a clearing on the wooded hillside called Sengedleah, meaning 'burnt lea', or 'the clearing made by burning'. It was the same clearing that was mentioned in Woodchester's Saxon charter that Ecglaf and Wulphun used to trace the bounds of the ancient estate. Several centuries before, the Romans cut timber from this same hillside to fire bricks and tiles for their villa and to fuel its hungry hypocaust. On the site of the Roman brickyard, where Little Britain Farm now stood, the young naturalists often found pieces of tile and brick that had been fired in the Roman kilns.

Edith Payne had inherited from her American father both a fondness for flowers and powers of minute observation characteristic of the true naturalist. She also had a reverence for butterflies, bees and other small creatures she found living amongst the wild flowers and grasses growing on Minchinhampton Common above St Loe's. Both the butterflies and wild flowers that abounded on the common in high summer she recorded in exquisite detail. When she had selected several different flowers to paint, she dug up the plants with some of the surrounding turf and took them back to her studio, where she arranged them on a saucer.

To obtain her butterfly subjects she went out on to the common towards sundown and picked the grass stems on which the insects were resting. She brought them back to the studio in a jam jar and placed them on the flowers in the saucer, put a glass-topped table over them, and painted them at first light the following morning. When she had finished with the butterflies, she let them go, taking them back to the place where she had found them resting. The flowers too she would replant where she had dug them up. Adonis blue against a backdrop of milkwort, daisies, wild thyme and grasses, or common blue resting on autumn gentian were among the many watercolours of this talented artist, but never did she discover the rare large blue.

The female large blue which had been laying her eggs in the thyme's flower buds now made her characteristic heavy, wobbling flight to another thyme-covered anthill. So regular was the large blue's appearance each sunny morning that it often coincided with the church clock's ten chimes, and so constant was its departure that this was accompanied by twelve strikes.

Other butterflies were lured from their resting places by the late morning sun. The first flush of meadow browns, not long freed from their pupal cases attached to grass stems, their brown and orange wings barely dry, flashed their eyespots at one another as they fluttered over the grasses. Along the edge of Dingle Wood courting pairs of speckled woods interrupted their flight to settle on leaves of bramble in the dappled sunlight and spread their sepia and cream wings, or to feed from its flowers with wings closed. Of all the butterflies to be seen around Woodchester, the speckled wood was the only one to fly from early spring to late summer, frequenting shady woodland rides and margins, lanes and hedgerows.

For the last few days, Gytha and her family had been living in the vicinity of Dingle Wood. As the church clock chimed half-past-three, the stoats left their den beneath the roots of an oak. High up in the tree a tawny owl hooted wistfully as a family of blue tits discovered its roost while searching for moth larvae amongst the young leaves. The royal hunters stood, with ears pricked, looking up in the direction of the mobbing titmice. In the wood's chequered sunlight their coats showed up dusky-brown above and white below, and the same white hairs covered their paws in varying amounts. Each young stoat sported a full black-tipped brush, which was longer in the dogs than the bitches, and which it constantly whisked to and fro.

Both Aethelbeorht and Aella seemed the most alert of the litter, and when Gytha was away from them, it was from these two that the others took their cues. As Aethelbeorht turned his gaze from the oak branches where the titmice mobbed the tawny owl, the rest of the litter followed likewise, and in close formation they all bounded off through the wood, pausing often to sniff Gytha's scent trail and to leave their own scent marks on fallen branches and along the worn paths made by badgers. This they did, not only by means of their strongly scented scats and urine, but by rubbing their hindquarters to deposit the oily secretion from the glands at the root of the tail. They frequently also scent-marked each other, particularly before they set off from their den on a hunting foray with their mother. Each stoat could recognise its own scent and that of each of its siblings, and could distinguish any of them from scent marks left by Gytha, Aethelwald or other stoats that frequented the wood. In this way the young royal hunters learned to find their way around the wood and other parts of the Dingle and to become familiar with the movements of other stoats.

The troupe moved through the wood under cover of bramble and the dense carpet of dog's mercury, often taking the same routes used by foraging badgers. In his eagerness to join his mother, Aethelbeorht galloped on ahead of the others. Gytha had gone down a rabbit hole beneath the fence that separated the wood from the rough pasture where the blue butterflies flew. He hesitated at the mouth of the burrow and sniffed at an ash root that Gytha had scent-marked before she went underground. Aella and the others soon caught up with their brother and gathered around the entrance, each investigating the root with their white-edged muzzles.

A pair of jays, accompanied by their five fledglings, alarmed the young stoats with their rasping cries, warning their young and other birds in the wood of the royal hunters they had spied in the undergrowth. The stoats stood transfixed at the sight of the birds with the colourful plumage that flew agitatedly from tree to tree, displaying their white rumps and bright blue wing flashes. Like its cousin the magpie, the jaypie had earned a reputation among gamekeepers and foresters as a pilferer of eggs and nestlings. Ever vigilant, this sagacious crow was even more elusive than the magpie, and on estates where a keeper was employed, it managed to steal many an egg from his pheasants or partridges before its carcass shared his gibbet with magpie, carrion crow, hedgehog, grey squirrel, weasel and stoat.

Cautiously, Aethelbeorht entered the rabbit hole, followed closely by Aella and one of her two brothers. The other three kittens stayed behind at the entrance, huddled together and waiting anxiously for the return of their mother. Apart from Gytha's scent trail and the earthy odour of the burrow, there were other unfamiliar and indiscernible smells that made the young stoats wary as they ventured into the hillside. Aethelbeorht kept close to the side of the burrow, which had been rubbed smooth by the regular passage of rabbits and other inhabitants of the warren. For a while he felt himself descending, then after he turned a bend, the burrow began to ascend steeply. Ahead of him he saw a faint shaft of light. It came from a scoot-hole which rabbits had opened to the surface in order to escape from royal hunters pursuing them below ground.

Before he reached the escape hole, Aethelbeorht came to an offshoot of the tunnel and went along it to investigate. After taking several paces in the pitch darkness, he found yet another branch and felt his way along the side of the burrow by detecting with his vibrissae minute eddies of air it produced as he progressed. He had not gone far when, from a blind-ending chamber, came a grunting and growling noise that made him start. In the nest chamber three rabbits were huddled together on a shelf of bare earth. A large buck, who was resting with two does, began to thump the floor with his hindfeet and to grind his bared teeth, making Aethelbeorht back off.

Aella and her other brother, uncertain about the strange smells and sounds they encountered, had already turned back, and with the rest of the litter were greeting Gytha, who had returned with a young rabbit she had killed in the warren. Undaunted, Aethelbeorht carried on exploring the burrow until he came to another scoot-hole. He stood in the pale beam of light, peering up into the near vertical shaft. His nostrils dilated as they tested the fresh air wafting into the burrow, and he began to climb up the steep wall of the pop-hole. When his head appeared above ground, he paused to look around, but all he could see was a forest of thorny stems, for he had surfaced in a bramble brake.

He climbed out of the escape hole and moved cautiously through the thicket, his young senses heedful of every new smell and sound. As he came to the edge of the brake, sounds reached his ears that he had not heard before. They were not like any warning cries or songs of birds he had come to know during the short time he had been living around the Dingle. He looked in the direction of the ancient track that followed the edge of Dingle Wood, his inquisitive head framed by bramble stems, bright eyes straining to see two figures coming into view.

Aethelbeorht had not yet met a human, even though the neighbourhood of the Dingle was a natural playground for the village children. As the two women approached, deep in conversation, the differing pitches and modulations of their voices and their gay summer dresses fascinated him and lured him out of the brambles into the grass. He sat up on his haunches to get a better view as the women came to within a few yards of him.

Lilian Cashmore, who was the more observant of the two, noticed a movement in the grass and motioned her friend to be quiet and to look towards the brambles. Aethelbeorht ducked down in the grass. He felt wary at the sudden cessation of sound as the women stopped talking. His nostrils caught another new smell, that of human scent. Yet it was mixed with one that reminded him of a smell he had met in Dark Wood where the lilies of the valley flowered. He raised himself up on his hindlegs to watch the taller of the women. As Lilian trod quietly through the grass, followed by her friend, the lily of the valley scent she was wearing masked her own. Her friend looked on as Lilian extended her gloved hand towards the wild animal. Aethelbeorht, feeling no fear, laid a white paw on her shoe. Seeing this, Lilian's friend became concerned for her safety and begged her to come away, for she believed in the reputation of stoats and weasels as bloodthirsty killers, who on occasions had been known to attack humans.

Lilian, who like many true country folk had a way with wild creatures, seemed to instil trust in the young stoat, for Aethelbeorht placed his other forepaw on her shoe and began to lick the soft calf leather. She froze, fascinated by the boldness of the beautiful creature with the glossy coat and dark appealing eyes, and marvelled at the lithe movements of its limbs, whose touch she barely felt. She watched the inquiring face with alert ears constantly twitching, their parchment thin linings a delicate translucent pink and fringed with fine, pale golden hairs. She saw too the brown velvety muzzle sprouting long sensitive whiskers, and the moist brown nose with ever-dilating and contracting nostrils. But most alluring of all were those dark, piercing, slightly bulbous eyes.

Suddenly, Aethelbeorht turned his head towards the wood. The brief spell of human attraction had been broken, for he had heard the shrill call of his mother, who had noticed he was missing from the litter. For a few moments he sat up on his hindlegs, his ears focusing the sound, and then he fell on to all fours and quietly and unhurriedly disappeared into the brambles.

On their way down the track, Lilian and her friend spoke animatedly about their encounter with the little stoat. For many years they had walked together on Sundays, between singing in the church choir at matins and evensong, and had caught fleeting glimpses of stoats, but never before had they seen one at such close quarters, nor one so seemingly fearless and trusting. They took a footpath that crossed Laggar Lane and descended the steep pasture of the Laggar on the south side of the Dingle. When they reached the stream, they sat down on the grass close to the levelled remains of the old brick bull pen.

While they carried on their conversation, they were oblivious of the mechanical song of the grasshopper warbler that sang from one of the alders. Its grasshopper-like song was more like the sound of the line running off an angler's reel, and the phrases were of such long duration that one wondered how such a tiny bird managed to find the breath to sustain them. The great parson-naturalist, Gilbert White of Selborne, said that even country folk laughed when he told them that the monotonous reel was the song of a bird. They had supposed it belonged to an insect, and in some parts the warbler had earned the name of cricket bird. As the cock bird sang, he held his mandibles wide apart, puffed out his little white throat and spread his tail feathers fanwise. All the time his head moved from side to side and his body quivered like some Victorian mechanical toy.

The hen bird was sitting on her brood of six eggs in a nest

of dead leaves and grasses, lined with fine roots and a few hairs, which the pair had built in a clump of rushes at the side of the stream. She was so careful not to give away the whereabouts of the nest, that she would creep mouse-like through the dense vegetation every time she left or returned to it. Of all the nests the young naturalists had looked for, that of the grasshopper warbler had so far eluded them. Almost a century before, the two Housman brothers from nearby Woodchester House, where they had their own natural history museum, had failed to find the nest of this most secretive of warblers.

As dusk fell over the Dingle, the grasshopper warbler still sang. Higher up the stream a water rail called out in alarm with a noise like a squealing pig, for a sow badger from one of the sets in Dingle Wood had taken her cubs to drink and had disturbed the roosting bird. High up in Dark Wood a cock pheasant honked as it watched the lame dog fox leave his lair to hunt, and at the wood's edge other badger cubs played around the spoil heap outside the entrance to their nursery. The young royal hunters had long slept off their last meal of rabbit, and they followed Gytha's scent trail as she led them alongside the tumbledown wall at the bottom of Dingle Wood on their first night hunt together.

Larchgrove

XIII

The weathercock on the church steeple stood still in the mild southerly wind, its golden plumage glowing in the rays of the evening sun. Down in the Dingle, young children played, paddling in the stream and building a dam below the footbridge with pieces of limestone collected from the shallow bed. Hidden from view in the thick streamside vegetation the grasshopper warbler sang its incessant, insect-like song. Overhead, swifts which nested in the church spire joined swallows to reap the rich harvest of flying insects emerging from pasture and woodland. As the sun went down over the dark Welsh hills beyond the silver Severn, noctule bats left their roosts in tree hollows to accompany the swifts and swallows in their aerial hunt above the treetops. The noctule, or great bat, matched the swift in its powerful flight, wheeling over the trees and plunging earthwards with shrill, metallic squeaks to capture beetle, moth and midge, before ascending again on long, slender wings.

As day turned into dusk, pipistrelles and horseshoe bats emerged from crowded roosts in the church spire and roof spaces of

Woodchester House and other old mansions to hunt over the Dingle. Unlike their cousin the noctule, both bats hunted close to the ground, twisting and diving to take their prey. In the deepening dusk, long-eared bats stirred at their roosts and left the church eaves, house attics and tree hollows to hunt among the trees of Dark Wood and Dingle Wood. Gliding along the woodland edge they paused frequently to hover and take a moth or beetle from the foliage. An hour after the first noctules had flown, the Daubenton's bat left waterside tree hollows to hawk for caddis flies and midges over the pond next to Southfield Mill.

Each kind of bat left its roost at its own allotted time, which was governed both by the time the sun set and the creature's internal clock. Also each occupied its own chosen niche where it could practise its particular way of hunting, so that there was less competition for prey or air space. These nocturnal predators took the insect bounty of high summer at the time when many of them were having young. Some that had given birth even carried their newborn young with them on their foraging flights.

The bats, like the royal hunter and other four-footed predators, had an ancestry that stretched back over many millions of years. Their earliest ancestors were nocturnal, shrew-like hunters that lived in the tropical rain forest when the dinosaurs ruled the earth. They climbed through the forest canopy in search of insects, often pursuing those that took flight by gliding from one tree to another by means of a membrane of skin on both sides of the body, stretched between fore- and hindlimbs. Eventually, this extension of the skin of back and belly became supported by the elongated bones of arm and hand to produce the parchment-like wing of the bat. The ultrasounds the primitive insectivores made to locate their nocturnal insect prey among the foliage became refined through the long passage of time, so that the bat tribe became as successful in the air and as diverse as the rodents on the ground.

As with the bats, dusk was also the signal for other, more elusive, nocturnal hunters of the Dingle to leave their dark daytime refuge. Soon after the noctule left its roost, the badgers from Dark Wood and Dingle Wood had emerged from their sets, for in high summer, when the nights were short, the animals needed more time to forage. But not all the Dingle badgers were abroad. On the north side of the combe, at the boundary of a field known as Home Ground, badgers had dug into a natural landslip of clay and limestone. Their galleries led beneath the garden of a house, which was one of several built on an adjacent field once known as Seven Acres. The set was isolated from Dark Wood and only partly shaded by a large ash, so the badgers that lived there tended to emerge a little later than their woodland neighbours.

From the track that led along the north side of Home Ground, the entrances to the set were hidden by dense thickets of bramble, elder and blithytwine, and around the margins of the spoil heaps grew thick clumps of pungent-smelling nettles. Many years of digging by generations of badgers had produced huge mounds of clay and limestone, which had been compacted by their feet into platforms of bare earth outside the entrances. Well-worn paths connected the half-dozen or so entrances, often passing through tunnels of bramble and under prostrate trunks of elder. Some paths led from the set to the badgers' feeding grounds and also to other sets in the Dingle, for the badger was the only social member of the weasel tribe.

In the branches of the ash tree, beneath whose spreading roots the badgers had dug their burrows, sat the two young naturalists. Just before sunset, they had climbed into the crown of the tree by means of a home-made ladder, and had been waiting patiently for a glimpse of the badgers. The two boys had learned how during the war years a schoolmaster from Rendcomb College at nearby Cirencester had revealed the secret life of the badger by watching and photographing the shy creatures at their sets. They had read his recent book on the badger and wanted to experience for themselves the excitement of seeing these elusive animals.

The boys had been sitting in the tree for over an hour and were becoming cramped and fidgety. They hoped any small noise they made as they tried to get more comfortable would not be heard by the badgers, for they had learned that, like their sense of smell, their hearing was acute. They had reasoned that since the night air was still and they were high above the set, the badgers would not detect their scent. They watched an entrance which they knew was well used. During the day they had noticed flies going in and out, and they found that some sticks they had placed vertically across the entrance the previous day had been knocked down. Also, outside the entrance there was some dried grass that had been dropped by a sow collecting fresh bedding. The young naturalists were growing impatient and were beginning to think the badgers would not show themselves, when suddenly, at the dark entrance, there appeared a black and white striped face. It seemed to be looking straight at the boys. Now the face disappeared, and the boys wondered if the badger's tiny eyes had sensed their presence in the tree. Perhaps, they thought, the animal was suspicious of the unfamiliar shapes among the branches. The boys dare not use the binoculars they had brought with them, for they knew the badger's eyes were especially sensitive to any slight movement.

Now the badger's face appeared once more, this time protruding further from the entrance. The watchers could make out the white head with the bold black eye stripes and the small white-tipped ears. It moved first in one direction, then in another, scenting the night air with its pig-like snout. The boys became tense with excitement, as it was the first time they had seen a badger. It came further out and sat and scratched the back of its neck with one of its hindfeet, for the animal was host to biting bugs that flourished in the bedding of the warm and humid sleeping chamber. In between the bouts of scratching it paused to look around and sniff the air.

Soon another badger appeared. By the way the first animal greeted it, the boys assumed this one was a sow. It seemed slimmer and had a narrower head and neck than what they supposed was the boar. Coming from inside the set the boys heard the cackling of cubs, a sound that reminded them of chattering magpies. By now the badger watchers' eyes had become accustomed to the darkness, so that they could make out four black and white heads moving around. One of the boys shone a torch fitted with a red filter at the badgers, whose eyes were supposed to be insensitive to red light. In the torch beam the animals appeared unperturbed, and now the boys could see they were a family group consisting of a broad-headed boar, a sleeker sow and two well-grown cubs.

It seemed certain to the boys that the badgers were oblivious of their presence in the tree, so one of them lifted his binoculars and looked at them bathed in the flood of red light. The large, light-gathering lenses of the ex-naval glasses brought the badgers to within several yards of the boy's eyes. He could see every detail of the animal, which seemed to be more bear-like and far removed from the royal hunter and other members of the weasel family, whose ancestors were small forest dwellers. This, the largest of all the weasels, had evolved a powerful frame to dig its fortress out of subsoil and rock, using the long bear-like claws of its sturdy forelimbs. Spending most of its life underground, and living mainly on small animals and plants, the badger was more of a forager than a predator, occupying a niche where it did not compete for a living with its wholly carnivorous cousins.

In centuries past, the badgers living in Woodchester's combes had cause to be wary of man, who hunted them with dogs, often taunting them with terriers in their sets and digging them out. The Anglo-Saxons, who called the badger 'Brock', relished its flesh and wore its hide. The fat they got after cooking the meat was used to preserve leather boots and gaiters as well as a cure-all for sore throats and rheumatics, and a badger's tooth was considered a lucky charm. Today, in Woodchester, the animals had little reason to fear the human inhabitants. Occasionally, badgers got the blame for taking newborn lambs, or an old boar would be suspected of killing a resident's chickens or ducks and taking the eggs. But more often than not the true culprit was a fox who shared the badgers' set. The only time the badgers discovered the strong smell of humans around their sets was sometimes in winter, when the woodmen from Workman's sawmills were extracting timber from the woods, or when men from the Berkeley Hunt had been stopping foxes' earths.

With the close proximity of human habitation to the Dingle, it was not unusual for the badgers living there to forage in nearby gardens, for these human plots had been claimed from ancient pasture that had been the hunting ground of past generations of badgers. One of the boys knew that badgers from the set they were watching visited his own gardens on the former Seven Acres. Sometimes the badgers dug up and ate young carrots, beetroot and potatoes, which they found more sweet and succulent than the tubers of pignut and cuckoo pint. The father of the boy had tried to protect his crops by putting up wire netting, but the badgers dug underneath it with their powerful paws. Now he had given up trying to keep off the badgers, for he supposed they did more good than harm by eating the grubs of garden pests hidden in the soil.

Jim Hammond, the milkman and farmhand at Fawkes' farm, found that by balancing an iron bar between two upturned buckets on his vegetable plot, the badgers stopped digging up his new carrots. He reckoned that an encounter with such a deterrent device reminded the animal of a large gin trap, for the badger had an innate fear of clanking iron throughout its long history of human persecution. Only once had one dislodged the iron bar as it plundered his plot, and since then he had no more thefts. Some people in the parish encouraged badgers into their gardens by leaving food out for them. In this way they became more trusting of humans and considered such gardens their rightful territory. The occasional loss of a few vegetables was a small price to pay for the privilege of having badgers in the garden and the pleasure these shy creatures gave to their human hosts.

From their lookout in the ash tree the young naturalists watched the badgers play. The two cubs chased each other round the spoil heap outside the entrance, each trying to grab the other's tail and showering the parents with soil and bits of old bedding. The boar and sow, who had been grooming each other, then joined in the game, each pushing its snout under a cub and flipping it over on to its back, for the badger was noted for the unusual strength of its neck muscles. It was commonplace for it to turn over heavy pieces of limestone that had fallen from a drystone wall in order to find a tasty beetle or slug hiding beneath.

The boys watched in amazement. They had not expected to see so much on their first badger watch. They did not know that all this rag-roustering was the badgers' way of strengthening the family bond. For the cubs, such boisterous play prepared them for adulthood, when they would need to display aggression towards badgers from other social groups. The badgers the boys watched belonged to the same social group, some other members of which occupied this same set, and these, a sow with her three cubs, had just emerged from another entrance out of sight of the watchers.

Suddenly, there was a commotion of whickering and yelps as the cubs from both families engaged in scuffles and chases, emitting into the warm night air their strong sweaty scent, which the watchers could detect. Before the two families moved off to forage, their members set scent on one another by backing up, raising their tails, and depositing musk from their musk glands. In this way the group acquired its own unique scent that was different from that of other groups living in the Dingle.

The badgers all took the same well-worn path from the set on to the track that followed the northern edge of Home Ground. They went at an ambling trot, heads down and noses to the ground, their wide hindquarters swaying from side to side. Each in turn would frequently pause to listen or to squat down and rub its scent on the ground. Such scent-marking enabled the animals to find their way to their feeding grounds and to retrace their steps back to the set. Through years of musking by generations of badgers, a network of scent trails was established that became badger highways. Some of these became so impregnated with scent that should one of them cross a field which later became ploughed, the badgers could still detect their scent and soon re-establish their former route.

On their way through Home Ground the badgers searched for dung beetles that visited the dung of cows pasturing there. They turned over dried cowpats and broke them up with their long front claws to get at the large beetles that ate and raised their young on the dung. And, in order to find those that had escaped into their burrows beneath the pats, they dug pits in the turf and seized them between their incisor teeth or licked them up with their tongues. Smaller kinds of beetle, whose larvae fed in large numbers beneath the pats, were also eagerly sought and consumed in equally large amounts, along with some of the adult beetles and earthworms that found refuge there.

A little way down the track the badgers passed a small spinney of hawthorn and ash in which a beekeeper had put some of his hives. Knowing the badgers' liking for honey, he had tied down the hive roofs to prevent the animals lifting them off with their noses. Now that it was the height of the main honey flow, bees inside the entrance were helping to ripen the honey by drawing a current of warm air over the honeycomb. Here household bees processed the nectar that foragers had collected from lime blossom, bramble and willowherb that abounded in the Dingle during July.

One of the badger cubs wandered off the track into the spinney, his nose drawn to the strong scent of bees and ripening honey that wafted from the entrance to one of the hives. Cautiously, the cub put his nose to the entrance, at which a vanguard of bees fanned their wings, and he recognised the scent that was familiar in the sleeping chamber of his set, where fermenting grass and other plants were used as bedding. The sudden appearance of the cub's nose and the smell of its breath at the hive entrance alerted guard bees, which stung him on the sensitive skin lining his nostrils, making him turn tail and rush back to the group yelping with pain. One of the cub's littermates had also been stung earlier in the month, and since then had always given the hives a wide berth. Yet despite the high risk of being stung, July was a month when the badgers eagerly sought after the nests of bumblebees and wasps.

The old boar, foraging along the bank between Home Ground and the garden of Larchgrove, had found the underground nest of the small earth bumblebee. Following his nose, he dug down into the nest, and in a few mouthfuls gobbled up the queen, her workers and brood, along with the honey-filled waxen cells that were a particular relish of the sweet-toothed animal. So swift was the badger's plunder of the nest that the torpid bees had no time to sting their nocturnal predator.

At the base of a wire netting fence alongside Larchgrove, the occupants of the house had made a badger gate, since they welcomed the animals into their garden. One by one, the badgers nosed the oak swing gate and squeezed through, and went single file across the lawn into a fir spinney at one corner of the garden. Here the badgers had dug their latrines in the dark, needle-covered soil. Most of the dozen or so pits were filled up with dung in various stages of decay. The latrines had been made by badgers from this same social group, and the scented dung they contained served as signals of ownership of their territory. The cubs looked on while the boar and the two sows dug out new pits over which they squatted, then they in turn deposited dung in the same pits. Earlier in the year, soon after the cubs were weaned, they learned from their parents to use the latrines when they were first brought above ground.

Badgers from the Dingle had always visited the four-acre garden of Larchgrove, a house with a 350-year-old history beginning with two Cotswold stone barns, and once occupying a plot known as Five Acres. The large, traditionally cultivated garden was a favourite foraging ground for the badgers, more for the earthworms, beetles and their grubs, slugs, snails, wireworms and leatherjackets that flourished in the manure- and compost-enriched, pesticide-free soil than for the vegetable produce it offered. Though, particularly during a summer drought, succulent carrots and peas were a welcome delicacy, and earlier in the season the asparagus bed was sometimes raided. In the summer too, the badgers dug out wasps' nests that were often built in a bank or between the drystone walling that surrounded a raised, round lawn, sometimes demolishing part of the stonework to reach the fat wasp grubs and even the adult insects. In the autumn they were regular visitors to the orchard, where they feasted on windfall apples and pears of many varieties. The residents of Larchgrove were well aware that they shared their garden with badgers, and in order to watch them at close quarters they fed them throughout the year on the back lawn.

From the open kitchen window the woman and her husband watched as the old boar led the other badgers from the fir spinney on to the back lawn, their bobbing black and white heads emerging one at a time from the darkness into the light from the kitchen. They stood or sat facing the house, their snouts scenting the air, for they were waiting to be fed. The boar waddled forward from the rest of the group and lifted his great bulk on to his hindlegs by placing his forefeet against the roughcast of the kitchen wall and pawing his way up until his long claws were gripping the windowsill. He stood there with his head nodding back and forth, scenting the loaf of locally baked bread that the woman was cutting up into half-slices. The boar was the most trusting member of the group and regularly came to the window to beg for food. But he was not just content with bread, and would not leave until he had received his great treat of several bourbon biscuits, taking each one from the woman's hand in his worn–down incisor teeth and canines and crunching it up with his equally worn molars.

The couple watched the other badgers feeding on the bread they threw out on to the lawn. Sometimes one or two badgers caught the bread before it hit the ground, so good was their sight in the feeble light. The experienced watchers also noticed that there was a definite pecking order among the group, for when the old boar was not begging for food at the kitchen window, he was always the first to feed when bread was thrown out on to the lawn, followed in turn by the two sows and their cubs.

In late May, when the parents first brought their cubs on to the lawn, the couple watched two cubs fighting over some bread and saw the boar pick one of them up by the scruff and shake it, after which the cub slunk off to the outside of the group. Then one of the sows picked up some bread and took it over to the cub, who seemingly had learned to behave after its admonishment.

In early February, the couple had noticed that the sows were heavily pregnant and were having difficulty climbing over the drystone wall into the garden, for then there was no badger gate. The sows would lumber on to the lawn, panting from the exertion of scrambling over the wall, and lie down, waiting for food to be thrown out. The boar would pick up half-slices of bread and take them to the sows, dropping them in an arc around their heads, and the sows would reach out and take a half-slice at a time. Each night that the badgers were fed they always seemed content with the same amount of bread, and they often left a few pieces on the lawn before going off to forage in the garden. What was left was sometimes taken by a fox who now and again shared the badgers' set, and who appeared intimidated by them, always remaining in the background while they fed.

Over a year of feeding and watching the badgers, the couple had learned to distinguish the various members of the group. Apart from the differences in build and shape of the head, the tail of the boar was less bushy and whiter than that of the sow, and there were subtle differences in the widths of the black and white head stripes of individuals and in the way their tails bent to the left or right. The watchers got to know individuals so well they had even given them names.

The couple watched the badgers take it in turns to drink from the birds' water bowl, for the bread had given them a thirst. As the church clock chimed half-past ten the badgers trotted off in the direction of the fir spinney, on their way making snuffle holes in the grass in search of beetles, and the fox came out of the shadows to snatch one of the remaining pieces of bread.

Since they could not see any more of the badgers, the young naturalists climbed down from the ash tree overhanging the set. As they walked home they talked about the next time they would go badger watching and take their friend with them, who would shortly be coming to spend the school summer holidays with his aunt and uncle at Larchgrove Cottage.

Larchgrove Cottage

XIV

The thirteen-year-old boy lay awake in bed at Larchgrove Cottage. Through the open window he listened to the cockerel crowing in the pound and the deep crooning call of a turtle dove coming from the large garden of the Lawn. The boy had slept in the same iron bed with its feather mattress while he had been an evacuee with his aunt and uncle six years before. Then he was safe from the German bombs and rockets that fell on his home town of Hounslow, where during the Blitz he had slept in an Anderson shelter at the bottom of the garden. Since the war he had spent part of his summer holiday at Woodchester, travelling up from Paddington on a steam train of the Great Western Railway, in care of the guard or some trusty fellow passenger. Each time he came to stay he imbibed more of the sights, sounds and smells that made up Longtree's unique natural history.

He lay thinking about the adventures he would have this summer holiday with his friends, birdwatching and hunting for fossils in the old quarries on Selsley Common, the walks and cycle rides he would take with his aunt Lilian, and flying a kite and model glider on Amberley. This holiday he planned to build yet another bigger and better glider to fly on those hot hazy days that seemed so much a part of summers in Woodchester. Then there was the famous Roman pavement to visit, which his Uncle Ernest had helped to uncover again for the first time since before the war.

Like the big house Larchgrove, Larchgrove Cottage had its own humble beginnings several centuries before, for it had grown up from a blacksmith's forge. The water that quenched the white-hot iron came from a well, which now lay capped beneath the flagstone floor of the single, small living room. The limewashed Cotswold stone and brick cottage had a high-pitched roof covered with heavy stone slates. On the first floor there were two bedrooms, the smaller of which was the boy's. There were a further two rooms in the attic, one with a dormer window, giving a fine view to Amberley and Minchinhampton, the other a box room lit by a skylight, which had been the boy's playroom since his evacuation. Here he would spend hours building model gliders and listening through headphones to the wartime Home Service on an old crystal set.

The boy's sleepy eyes were attracted to the familiar ornamental smoking pipe that hung from the white distempered plaster wall above the bed, its rose-tinted glass gleaming in the early morning light. On the opposite side of the room stood a pine washstand with a white marble top, on which stood a matching jug and bowl. Beyond this was a dark-stained pine door with its simple latch. The boy heard the sounds of cows at the end of Watery Lane where it joined Selsley Road, the clatter of their hooves on the tarmac and the occasional loud low, answered by the coaxing calls of George Fawkes, the cowman. Then he heard the quickening pace of the herd as it made its way down the hill to Fawkes' farm.

During his holidays the boy often helped to bring in the cows from Oxlease or Shortcombe meadow for the afternoon milking, or take them back to the field afterwards. He could picture the individual cows in the small herd. He had particularly poignant memories of a blue roan shorthorn called Bluebell who broke her front legs falling over on the steep icy road during the harsh winter he had spent at Woodchester during the war. He held a clear image in his mind of the hapless beast being hauled on to a sled and pulled by the farm horse to the farmyard. He remembered seeing the prostrate animal shot through the head with a humane killer, watching its death throes, legs flailing, and the sudden expulsion of acrid-smelling urine over the concrete floor of the barn. And he would never forget the dark red blood that surged from the cow's cut throat to form a huge pool over the floor, and afterwards the hauling by the heavy horse of the great carcass with the large, staring, lifeless eyes and lolling tongue on to the waiting hunt wagon. This was a natural part of the country scene, which even young children were brought up to accept without cosseting.

As the church clock chimed half-past six, the boy heard the front door of the cottage open and close, the creak of the iron front garden gate, and the grate of his uncle's hobnailed boots on the road as he went to work in the garden of Larchgrove. Then he was aware of Jim Hammond's horse-drawn milk cart outside, the clank of churns, again the squeal of the gate's hinges and the sounds of his aunt's milk can being filled and set down on the Welsh slate flag of the front porch, which was made of quarter-sawn larch, overhung with honeysuckle and a perfumed yellow rose. As he drifted back to sleep, the boy was just conscious of the sound of hooves as the horse pulled the milk cart past the cottage and into the long driveway leading to Larchgrove.

After another hour the boy woke to the sound of the bedroom door latch being lifted and his aunt telling him it was time to get up. He could smell the bacon and eggs she was cooking in her little kitchen directly below his room, for soon his uncle would be returning for his breakfast. He quickly dressed, knowing his aunt was one for punctuality, and he descended the steep, dimly lit stairs that led to the living room. He lifted the latch and opened the door. Stepping down into the room, he was greeted by his uncle coming through the adjacent, low-lintelled back door, which led to the garden and which always seemed to be in use.

The boy climbed the slate steps that were set in the steeply terraced back garden, past the wash house with its coal-fired copper, and where his aunt kept her chicken feed, some garden tools and a pair of snowshoes hanging from the whitewashed wall. Standing on the path at the top of the steps that led to the little brick privy, he could see over to Amberley where he flew his glider, and he saw the weathercock on the church steeple glinting gold in the July sun. This same fine view Lilian would delight in when she rested on a green-painted wood and wrought iron bench that stood on the tiny lawn.

The elevated, sunlit garden was divided by two transverse cinder paths into neat, rectangular plots for fruit and vegetables and herbaceous flowers. These paths joined up with the one leading to the privy and the wood and corrugated iron coal and log store, and with another at the opposite side of the garden. This ran alongside a low drystone wall between the potting shed at the top of the garden and an iron gate opening on to Selsley Road by the entrance to the pound.

The soil was a dark grey, crumbly clay loam, whose fertility had been maintained over many years by regular applications of rotted chicken manure, garden compost, soot and lime, and not least by its excellent drainage into the underlying limestone. It supported a fine assortment of year-round vegetables, from onions to asparagus, soft fruit such as blackcurrants and redcurrants, cooking and wine-red dessert gooseberries, raspberries and strawberries, and an apple tree grown as a cordon against a wire trellis. The produce that Lilian grew herself, along with what Ernie was given by his employers at Larchgrove, kept the couple in fruit and vegetables throughout the year.

The flowers of Larchgrove Cottage were typical of the traditional cottage garden. Mostly they were to be seen in a border alongside the lower path that ran past the pound. In high summer, there were intense blue delphiniums, white, pink and crimson hollyhocks, Japanese anemones, marigolds, nasturtiums, columbines, and sweet-scented stocks that attracted night-flying moths. And in spring there were numerous snowdrops and crocuses that provided early pollen for honeybees from hives in neighbouring gardens.

The boy found it no hardship to have to use the garden privy, which he had to flush with rainwater taken in a white enamel bucket from a butt outside the door. This was replenished with water draining from the roof of Larchgrove's brick coach house and apple store that backed on to the mortared limestone wall of the cottage garden. While ensconced within the privy's whitewashed walls the boy would watch the habits of spiders that lurked in crannies, waiting for prey to become ensnared in their gossamer threads. Nor did he mind having to wash in cold rainwater drawn from the large tank that took the run-off from the cottage roof.

Under a lean-to glass roof outside the back door, where a wire gauze meat safe hung, stood an enamel wash bowl on its green-painted metal stand complete with soap, scrubbing brush, flannels and towel. It was here that the boy washed his hands after each visit to the privy, and at other times when he could not get to the kitchen sink, which his uncle used for washing and shaving and in which his industrious aunt always seemed to be washing up. His weekly hot bath was in a tin hip bath, which required the boiling of countless kettles on the gas stove. When not in use, the bath was stowed away in the kitchen, under the stairs, along with the haybox and other household utensils whose identity the darkness would not easily disclose.

The highly polished oak gateleg table at which the boy sat with his uncle and aunt at breakfast smelled of beeswax and turpentine. This, mixed with the smell of bacon, Ernie's working clothes and hair oil, imparted a sort of pleasant musky odour to the atmosphere of the living room, which like the rest of the cottage was a paradigm of homeliness. It was the room where the couple ate, rested, read or listened to the radio, and where friends and acquaintances were often welcomed through the front door, which was invariably found ajar.

The room was furnished mainly with items that had been bought at country house sales, and they left a bare minimum of floor space. The main focus of the room was the fireplace, which was situated on the end wall that abutted on to the pound. Above the mantelpiece, on which stood a clock, brass candlesticks, other small treasured ornaments and a photograph of the boy's late paternal grandfather, hung a large framed certificate recording Ernie's membership of the Royal Antediluvian Order of Buffalos, of which he was a leading light down at the ancient Royal Oak every Friday night. On either side of the fireplace was an alcove fitted with cupboards and bookshelves above. On top of the cupboard on one side stood Lilian's beloved wireless, and next to it an open Anthony Trollope novel.

Along the eighteen-inch-thick back wall, partly below a window that looked out on to the raised back garden, stood an old, hard-sprung chaise longue covered with a rug and cushions, on one of which the blue-grey Persian cat nestled. Pushed hard up against almost half the length of the chaise longue was the oak table with three mahogany dining chairs, the fourth standing against the wall by the front door and next to an oval mahogany glove table.

On the same side of the room, next to the fireplace, with its rag hearth rug, was Ernie's armchair, upholstered in leather and protected against the soiling effect of his working clothes and perspiration by lace-edged back and arm covers. Behind was a single front window with a maidenhair fern occupying the deep sill. The window gave a view to the road, beyond the iron front gate and railings, which, along with a short box hedge, enclosed the north-facing, narrow front garden, in which grew pyracantha, Welsh poppies and a large, luxuriant shield fern.

Through the window, when sitting on her chaise longue, Lilian was able to check on the movements of neighbours trudging up the steep hill laden with shopping from Stroud or the village store. Some were often asked in for a cup of tea and an opportunity to exchange the latest news. Also, through this window, in winter, she got endless pleasure from watching the birds that came to the table standing in the flower border up against the wall.

The front door, set in a low-linteled doorway that necessitated all but the shortest of persons to stoop, was hung inside with a heavy green baize curtain to keep out the draughts, especially when a north wind blew. In the corner, between the front door and the kitchen door, stood a wooden coat, hat and umbrella stand, which displayed an assortment of everyday coats, caps and hats, along with several hazel and ash walking sticks. Along the inside wall, between the kitchen door and that which led to the stairs, stood a dark oak sideboard in which the aunt kept her cutlery, table linen and best crockery. On the sideboard stood two Staffordshire figures on horseback, of the type which graced countless households at that time, and on the wall above hung a set of decorated china milk and cream jugs of varying capacities.

The breakfast the boy ate that morning was all home-produced. The home-cured bacon his aunt had brought back after a recent visit to her home village in the Vale of Evesham, where her family still kept a pig in a sty. The egg had been laid the same morning by one of the Rhode Island Red hens that scratched around in the parched earth of the pound, and the bread had been baked in a coke-fired oven at Garraway's bakery down the road. There was strong tea with milk from Fawkes' farm, and home-made marmalade or raspberry jam to follow.

Having been in service to two great-granddaughters of Josiah Wedgewood (cousins of Charles Darwin), who once lived at Southfield Mill House, Lilian was an excellent cook, and she was renowned for her rabbit pie or stew and Lord Woolton's carrot cake. There were always treats when the boy's friends were invited to tea, for then there was milk jelly, trifle made with garden-grown soft fruits served with thick unpasteurised cream, raspberry jam sponge and rich fruit cake, and the famous home-made ginger beer cool from the pantry. Such fine fare the boy had always been accustomed to at Larchgrove Cottage, even when it was his home during the last year of the war, as it had also been for two of his three elder brothers earlier in the war.

Unbeknown to the boy, the cottage had once been owned by a past resident of Woodchester, Edward Tuppen Wise, who, since boyhood, had been a bosom friend of A E Housman. In 1926, Wise bought the cottage, mainly for the pound that was attached to it, since the parish council, on which he served, gained revenue from the rent that owners of lost cattle and sheep had to pay to claim their livestock. He also let the cottage to Ernest and Lilian Cashmore, who eventually bought it after his death from his executors for £200, which was a loan from the Hounslow boy's mother.

Housman's mother, Sarah Jane, was one of ten children of the Rev Dr John Williams, rector of Woodchester during the first half of the nineteenth century. He was also a classical scholar and poet, like his grandson Alfred, and was descended from the same Devonian family on his mother's side as Francis Drake. Housman's godmother was Mrs Wise, mother of Edward Tuppen and his two sisters, Edith Madeline and Wilhelmina Harriette. It was Edith with whom Housman became infatuated and whom he had hoped to marry. After the early death of his mother, the young Housman spent his school holidays with the Wise family, who then lived at Woodchester House, where his young naturalist cousins had once lived. Housman treated Woodchester House as his second home, and all through his life he was drawn to the warm companionship of the Wises and took solace in the countryside of Woodchester.

After the death of their parents, the Wise children fell on hard times and they were forced to move to a less commodious home, Oakley House, which had been built on part of the five-acre plot belonging to Larchgrove. Because they had to take in paying guests, there was no room for Housman to stay, so he was found lodgings at a house called Ferndale, just below Larchgrove Cottage, whenever he spent holidays with the Wises. It was while staying with a Mrs Yorke at Ferndale in 1914, during a week's holiday from Cambridge, that he corrected the proofs of *A Shropshire Lad*. During his summer stay in 1926, while the Roman pavement was open, the diffident professor was persuaded to give a fortnight of informal lectures on life in the Roman villa, employing his unique knowledge of the classics. After his sisters had died, Edward Tuppen Wise moved to Elmsleigh, near the parish church, where he died in 1934 at the age of eighty-three, a few months after the seventy-five-year-old Housman's last visit to his old friend.

After breakfast the boy called for his friend who lived in an old terraced cottage called Lower Court, a former courthouse, a little way down from his aunt's. As he passed Ferndale, he heard familiar sounds coming from a shed in the garden, where blind Alec Howell, bell-ringer and village cobbler, carried on his craft, accompanying his hammer blows at the last with the same old whistled tunes. Together the two boys made for Fawkes' farm, where they hoped they would be given some interesting jobs, like helping to muck out the milking parlour, not for monetary reward but rather just for being made to feel useful. During past summers the boy had helped with the harvest and plum-picking, and in the year of his war evacuation there had been the back-breaking task of potato-picking, when the whole village school was closed for a week at the beginning of October.

This particular morning George and Basil Fawkes were loading a churn of milk on to the cart, along with an assortment of mops and rags, for they were going to the old churchyard where the Roman pavement had been uncovered and opened to visitors. As the boys rode on the horse-drawn cart they learned about the significance of the churn of full-cream milk and the mops and rags. They were told that milk had probably been used by the Romans to polish their mosaic floors, the fat in the milk acting like modern liquid wax floor polish and highlighting the natural muted colours of the tesserae.

They arrived at the old churchyard, where some visitors had

already come to view the Great Orpheus Pavement, as it had come to be known, and they drove through the open gates along the yew-lined avenue to the site of the pavement. The boy had been told by his aunt about the pavement, how it was supposed to be the finest of its kind unearthed in this country, and how proud the village felt to possess such a treasure. His uncle had first helped to uncover it in 1926, under the direction of Edward Tuppen Wise. At that opening, and at the one in 1935, he had taken it in turns with other members of the pavement gang to be nightwatchman in the churchyard, to prevent souvenir hunters taking pieces of the mosaic, which was on open display for several weeks. And this year too he would take his turn to keep guard for part of the night.

An enthusiastic band of over a hundred volunteers had uncovered the pavement by removing some 200 tons of soil, which had been dug up and replaced several times since the first complete excavation by Samuel Lysons in the late 1790s. As Recorder of Antiquities for George III, he had excavated the Roman villa and the pavement at the request of Mr Wathen of the Farms (now the Old Priory), working during the winter in a tent given by his friend Sir Joseph Banks, the naturalist who accompanied Captain Cook on his voyage round the world.

The boy stood at the edge of the excavation, in awe of the sight before him several feet below ground level. Though there were large areas of the pavement missing, where graves had been dug through it over several hundred years, it seemed to him like a great stone carpet of the most intricate design. Surely, he thought, his aunt's living room carpet would fit many times into its almost fifty-foot-square area. Beyond the repeated geometric patterns in red, white, cream, blue-grey and brown, which made up the broad border of the pavement, his eyes were drawn more towards the central circular procession of animals. Of the twelve animals that were thought to be depicted when the villa was standing, he could recognise the six surviving ones – a maned lion, followed in turn by a tigress, stag, leopard, wild boar and mythical griffon.

The only remaining part of Orpheus was his left knee, on which rested his lyre. Through his favourite classes in Latin, the classics and music at grammar school, the boy was familiar with the stories of the legendary poet and musician who charmed the wild beasts by accompanying his singing on a golden lyre.

The boy watched with his friend as the farmers carried the milk churn down on to the pavement and tipped out its creamy contents, which they spread over the entire area with the mops and rags. The wet surface of the hundreds of thousands of tesserae suddenly lost their drab look and took on a new life. After the milk had dried in the warm sunshine, giving off a smell reminiscent of the milking parlour at Fawkes' farm, the pavement's colours looked as they might have done those fifteen or more centuries ago.

The colours of the tesserae were due to the variety of stone from which they had been fashioned. Apart from the fine-grained white Carrara marble that the Roman mosaicists brought from Italy, there was white and cream-coloured limestone from Cotswold quarries and various shades of blue-grey limestone from the Severn Vale. Brown tesserae had been cut from Old Red Sandstone, of a similar kind to that from which the drinking trough in Watery Lane was carved. The red tesserae had been made from firing the same sort of yellow clay that was used to make the tiles and bricks for the villa.

That such a date could be given for the villa and its pavement was partly due to the discovery during its various uncoverings of many Roman coins, including one from Hadrian's reign and one, found only during the last week, bearing the laurel-wreathed head of Emperor Constantine. The boy wondered what it would have been like to have lived in Woodchester in Roman times and what famous feet might have trod the hypocaust-heated floor of that great hall. Perhaps, he thought, they might have belonged to personalities from the pages of his school Latin primer!

Old Dovecote of Woodchester House

XV

A peal of Grandsire Doubles resounded throughout the Dingle, the dry August air carrying the sound of the church's six bells far beyond the parish. Walking alongside Dingle Wood, the boy from Larchgrove Cottage and his two young naturalist friends watched a silver-washed fritillary fly with quick wingbeats in search of bramble blossom. But they didn't see the chequered orange and brown butterfly settle to feed from a blackberry flower, for the undersides of its closed hindwings, with their powder-like silver streaks, transformed the insect into a mouldering beech leaf that defied detection.

The butterfly had recently emerged from its chrysalis, and like the ubiquitous meadow brown, which rose from the grass at every step the boys took, had lived through the past winter as a young larva. In early spring it crawled away from its silken pad in a bark crevice to seek the tender young leaves of dog violet that grew on the woodland floor. The butterfly's survival had been ensured by the coppicing of ash and hazel as well as by the felling of mature timber, so allowing more light to reach the leaves of the larva's food plant.

In the heat of late morning few rabbits were out feeding in the fields bordering Dingle Wood and Dark Wood. Those that weren't resting, grooming or re-ingesting their own soft pellets in the cool of their burrows, soon retreated underground on seeing the three small human figures approach. Despite the fact that the Dingle was regularly grazed by rabbits, there were many wild plants which the insatiable animals avoided and left to flower. The rabbits' preference was for the short succulent turf that grew close to the woods and hedgerows, and whose luxuriant growth was maintained by their close cropping and constant manuring.

At the edge of Dark Wood and along the hedgerows and small fields, close to thickets of bramble that concealed burrow entrances, grew lady's bedstraw, whose panicles of tiny, bright yellow, stellar flowers smelled of ripening honey. Legend has it that the Virgin Mary lay on a bed of these same flowers in the stable at Bethlehem because the donkeys had eaten all the hay, and so the plant got its name. In Elizabethan times it was used along with hay for mattress fillings to dispel rank smells. And as for its herbal cures, it was said to be responsible for a multitude, including those for epilepsy and gout.

Burdock, with its hooked buds and flower heads, which, sticking to the fur of foxes and badgers, aided the plant's dispersal, grew alongside the blue clustered bellflower, yellow rockrose and mauve musk thistle, whose strongly scented nectar attracted burly bumblebees. Wild marjoram too had grown up unhindered by the discerning palate of the rabbit. It was of this sweet-smelling herb that the Roman poet Virgil wrote, telling how Venus, the goddess of love, carried off Ascanius to the groves of Idalin and set him down on a bed of wild marjoram. Since the ancients regarded the plant as a symbol of happiness, wedding couples in recent times were garlanded with it. But no plant was so obviously avoided by the rabbit as the ragwort. With its yellow, daisy-like flowers, it stood in clumps far out into the pasture, shunned by rabbits because of its own defensive poison, which browsing yellow and black-striped caterpillars of the cinnabar moth assimilated into their own tissues in order to render them unpalatable to predators.

The boys stood watching a buzzard soaring high above the Dingle. It was one of a pair that had nested in Dark Wood, on the southern side of Selsley Road, and it was hunting for rabbits as its forebears had done ever since the introduced coney had been kept in man-made warrens. When the first Saxon charter for the parish of Woodchester was granted by King Aethelbald of the southern Angles sixteen centuries before, one of its landmarks was stated as haboccumb, or hawk's combe, for this winged hunter had always nested on the wooded wold. Three centuries after the charter, in Domesday Book, a hawk's eyrie was named in the neighbouring parish of Avening. And in relatively recent times, only one hundred and fifty years ago, a field on Rodborough was known as ernscumb, meaning eagle's combe.

In those days that most graceful of hawks, the kite or glead, soared over the wold, as it had done during the Stone Age. Like vultures, the birds would have picked clean the mourned members of farming families whose dismembered corpses were left on the hillside until only their bare bones remained. These were then interred in a Cotswold stone vault beneath a mound of rubble and soil. When the wold was home to large flocks of sheep, the kite would scavenge stillborn lambs, afterbirth and the carcasses of dead animals. Today, the only reminder that the Anglo-Saxon glead once inhabited these southern parts of the wold until a century or more ago is to be found in the name Kite's Nest, given to a wood or even a lane.

The boy from Larchgrove Cottage saw how the buzzard glided in wide spirals, its broad, outstretched wings buoyed up by thermals, in just the same way that his model glider flew, and the manned machines that one day he hoped he might fly in. As the buzzard descended towards the wood, he could make out the upturned wing tips, feathers parted like outstretched fingers. In one wing he noticed there was a larger than normal gap between the feathers, and he wondered if the barred brown and cream feathers he had picked up a few days before had come from this same moulting bird. He was also curious as to how the buzzard could manage to see its prey from such a great height. Perhaps, he thought, it had telescopic vision.

Perched in a beech tree on the eastern edge of Dark Wood, overlooking the slope known as Sunny Bank, the buzzard sat sentinel, the streaked and barred plumage of its underparts blending with the sun-speckled foliage. It turned its head to watch a jay fly out of the wood, flashing its white rump and uttering its harsh 'skaaak, skaaak' call. With its large, forward-pointing eyes, the hawk could distinguish the jay's vinaceous plumage and the azure and black wing coverts, for its acuity of colour vision was inherited from its long extinct reptilian ancestors, the predatory, egg-laying dinosaurs that lived one hundred million years ago.

A big old buck rabbit emerged from the warren in full view of the buzzard. Despite his large eyes and an ability to see over more than one hundred and eighty degrees, the rabbit only saw in subdued shades of grey and could not detect the immobile form of the buzzard in the tree. But as the bird moved its head to preen under its wing, the rabbit was quick to see the movement. He stopped grazing, lowered his ears, and cowered low in the grass, for he had recognised his old arch-enemy. The buzzard tilted its head and brought the rabbit into sharp focus, but it could see it was too large an animal to tackle. The hawk's piercing gaze was now directed beyond the hedgerow bordering the southern edge of Sunny Bank, across Earl Ducie's Coneygre, towards the old withy bed. Despite the distance, the predator could make out flurries of russet and white, and the occasional whisk of a black-tipped tail, moving rapidly through the long grass at the edge of the brambles. The buzzard had spotted Gytha and her family of six.

The stoats had spent the last five weeks living in the vicinity of the Dingle, making their dens in drystone walls, rabbit burrows and tree hollows. Almost four months had passed since Gytha had given birth. Now that she had brought up her six surviving youngsters to learn to kill for themselves, she no longer did all the hunting or always led them on forays. Increasingly, she felt her former vigour of young motherhood was gradually waning, and she sensed the maternal ties with her offspring were weakening. Not so often did her young feel the need to suckle, and her teats had almost shrivelled to their former size. The height of summer's searing heat seemed easily to sap her strength, so that she spent more of the day resting. Her appetite too was not so keen, and she was often content to scavenge the scant remains of kills made by her rapidly growing family.

The four dog stoats were all larger than the two bitches, their heads being broader and their bodies longer by almost a half. Their tails also were longer and bushier, with more pronounced black tassels. All six stoats had grown out of their downy, chocolate-coloured kitten coats and now wore sleek summer pelts of rich reddish brown. Apart from being slightly more powerfully built than his three brothers, Aethelbeorht could be distinguished from them by subtle differences in his markings. On the darker fur of his noble head there were two small white flashes above his nose, and on each side of his creamy-white throat, below each ear and behind the angle of his strong jaws, was a small, round, brown spot. One of his brothers had three tiny white flecks between the eyes, but the other two had no such markings, neither were there any such distinguishing marks on the bitches' coats. Yet, under a discerning eye, each stoat could be identified by the varying amount of white fur covering its paws. But it was in personality that their differences were most apparent.

From an early age, Aethelbeorht had always been more precocious and daring than his three brothers, and such was the character of Aella, which set her apart from her only surviving sister. Since that fateful day when a sparrowhawk had taken her weakly sister, as Gytha led the family across Selsley Road to new hunting grounds, the young royal hunters had grown more vigilant of the hawks that hunted over the warrens of the Dingle. Invariably, the stoats would hunt from close cover or kill their prey underground. But sometimes, confident of their ability to evade or outwit their winged enemies, they seemed to delight in communal hunting, some of them flushing rabbits from their burrows, while others ambushed them as they bolted. At its perch on the edge of Dark Wood, the ever-watchful buzzard had witnessed such events over the past weeks, and it now waited in anticipation as the stoats made tracks along the edge of Coneygre.

Aethelbeorht and his three brothers galloped ahead, Gytha following a short way behind with Aella and her sister. As they bounded through the grass, flourishing their black-tipped tails, they would frequently pause to scent the many rabbit runs that led from beneath the brambles. Throughout their progress the buzzard held the stoats in its steady gaze. It saw clearly each member of the troupe as it crossed over a gateway leading to the field called Home Ground. Here they smelled the fresh foot scent of the three young naturalists who had recently passed that way. For a moment the stoats were lost to the buzzard's view as they ran into the cover of the brambles growing alongside the hedge dividing Sunny Bank from Coneygre. The hedge was a remnant of the former eastern extent of Dark Wood, before it was cut down to make way for sheep pasture many years ago.

The old buck rabbit stopped feeding and sat up on his stout haunches to get a better view of the movement he had noticed at the bottom of Sunny Bank. His keen nostrils sampled the air, which being so still carried no scent that could be associated with danger, and he dropped on to all fours again to resume feeding, his ears ready to detect any untoward sound. The buzzard, which had momentarily dozed in the heat, woke and blinked several times. Unlike the rabbit, the view it had from its elevated perch enabled it not only to notice movement, but to see clearly the cause of the commotion in the hedge bottom. Simultaneously, the buzzard focused its feathered ears and telescopic eyes on the

spot where Aethelbeorht had hold of a rabbit. The animal had
been bolted by Aella and her sister hunting through the labyrinth
of burrows that penetrated the ochre Cotswold sand beneath the
hedgerow at the top of Coneygre. The buzzard heard the big
buck rabbit thump his powerful hindfeet on the ground to warn
others that had begun to emerge from their holes.

At the bottom of Sunny Bank Aethelbeorht tussled with the
young rabbit as it struggled to break free from his deadly embrace.
The rabbit's piercing squeals could be heard by the three young
naturalists as they paddled in the cool spring water of the Dingle
stream several fields away. The buzzard stirred on its perch, ruffled
its feathers, and spreading its huge wings glided over the field,
its eyes set on the motionless form of the rabbit. For a moment
the rabbit had escaped Aethelbeorht's grasp with a single shallow
neck bite from his canines. It crouched low, its heart palpitating
violently and eyes closed. Aethelbeorht stood on his hindlegs a
leap away, poised to go in for the kill. But, seeing the broad-
winged buzzard suddenly bearing down on him, he turned tail
and fled down the same hole from which his prey had bolted.

The buzzard landed, the splayed talons of one foot closing
round the rabbit's trembling nape, and before its wings had come
to rest, it carried off its booty to a shady spot at the edge of
Dark Wood. After a short while, Aethelbeorht appeared at the
same hole and ran to the spot where the buzzard had thwarted
his attempt to make a kill. For several minutes, while the buzzard
devoured the rabbit, Aethelbeorht dashed about in a frenzy,
chattering with rage, his nose close to the ground in a effort to
locate his paralysed prey, unaware that it was being eaten by the
buzzard at the top of Sunny Bank.

As the tenor bell summoned latecomers to matins, some of
the young stoats harried their prey through the underground maze
of the warren. Taking care to avoid the slashing teeth and claws
of nursing does, they singled out young rabbits from earlier litters,
which were several times heavier than even the larger dog stoats.
The young royal hunters were set on satisfying their innate blood

lust, which was triggered by an abundance of prey. The burrows became filled with the nauseous scent of the stoats' musk, which some keepers and rabbit catchers likened to the smell of the acetylene gas that some villagers still used to power their cycle lamps, and which was said to strike terror in a rabbit. On hearing the familiar clatter of the rampaging stoats, their sharp-clawed paws scraping against the smooth-walled floor of the burrow, and the unmistakable whiff of their musk, rabbits either froze in their forms, huddled over their young with weapons at the ready, or bolted from their holes into the open. Such panic would also have been wreaked on the rabbits of old by the stoat's close cousin, the foul-smelling polecat, or foumart, which once plagued the warrens of Woodchester and the livelihoods of its warreners and rabbit catchers.

Aella bit into the neck of a young doe, at the base of the left ear. With an ever-increasing compression of her jaws, her canines sunk deeper into the muscle and penetrated the base of the thin-walled skull till they pierced the hindbrain. Death came quickly to the rabbit, yet the heart still beat sufficiently to pump blood through the wound, and on this Aella gorged herself. When she had finished feeding, and the heart had stopped beating, a circular bloody patch the size of a halfpenny was left behind the ear where the fur and skin had been chewed away by her incisor teeth.

Above ground, some rabbits scuttled from their holes into the bright sunlight, while others sauntered to the surface as though dazed or resigned to their imminent fate. In a flash, Aethelbeorht, who had been lying in wait, pounced on a three-quarter grown rabbit and quickly dragged it, squealing, down another hole, for he was determined not to be cheated again by the opportunist buzzard. In the security of the burrow his canines smashed the bone of the rabbit's second neck vertebra and lacerated the vulnerable spinal cord that ran through it. Opening up the wound with his chisel-like incisors, he lapped up noisily the blood which the failing heart pumped out, till the white fur of his lips was coated crimson.

Watched by the big buck and four other adult rabbits, Aella's sister followed the trail of her quarry over Sunny Bank, twisting and turning between ragwort and thistle. So intent was she in keeping to the rabbit's erratic line that she didn't notice the buck rushing towards her. As she caught up with her stupefied prey, and was about to spring on to its back, the buck made a sudden charge, butting her in the side with such force that she was flung into the air, turning head over tail and landing on her feet several yards distant. But she was determined to secure her quarry, and dodging further onslaughts from the buck, she cast around in an endeavour to pick up the rabbit's line.

The buzzard, satiated by its meal of rabbit, surveyed the slaughter on Sunny Bank where, after the stoats had left the scene, the corpses of six rabbits lay. From each one only a meal of blood had been taken, for each bore the telltale bloody mark behind one ear. But by the next morning not one body would remain, for they would become food for crow, buzzard, fox and badger, and already blow flies had discovered the bodies and laid their eggs around the wound and on the bared lips.

At the margin of the marsh that marked the site of the upper millpond, which the young naturalists called 'the bog', they watched a large dragonfly hawk up and down in search of prey. The primitive insect predator, a mere miniature of its ancestral Coal Age giant, was hunting gnats and mosquitoes that hatched in hordes from the swamp. As it flew past them, the boys heard the rustle of its large, cinnamon, membranous wings, but only when it settled on a meadowsweet flower did they notice its huge, dark blue compound eyes and similar coloured markings along the sides of its dingy brown body. Names such as mosquito hawk, horse stinger, and devil's darning needle had been given to the insect that spent two years as a wingless nymph in the reed-fringed lower millpond, where it hunted aquatic creatures as large as fish fry, itself often falling prey to voracious young pike.

The water-loving plants fringing the bog also had their own country names. Great willowherb, with its magenta, trumpet-shaped flowers, was known as codlins-'n-cream, since the fragrance of its flowers or crushed leaves was said to be reminiscent of the smell of cooking apples. Meadowsweet, whose creamy flowers gave up their heady scent to the warm air, was known to the Anglo-Saxons as medeswete, because it was used to flavour their mead, a drink made from fermented honey. Marsh marigolds, or May-blobs too, whose yellow buttery blossoms, now over, were the Mary-buds known to Shakespeare, and which farmers used to hang over their cattle byres on May Day to protect them from fairies and witches. There was hardly a plant thriving on the fertile clay of the Dingle that had not been named and held in high regard by past residents of Woodchester for its culinary or medicinal virtues, or to assuage their superstitious fears.

The two young boys made for the old dovecote that stood at the bottom of the Dingle, outside the walled garden of Woodchester House. Built of brick and roofed with Cotswold slates, the dovecote belonged to Woodchester House and had once been a source of pigeon meat. It was here that a barn owl sometimes roosted; a fact well known to the enquiring young naturalists, who now climbed up into the loft to see if they could find any owl pellets on the wooden floor.

Buzzard's tail feather

164

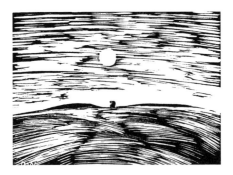

The Toots long barrow, Selsley Common

XVI

In the light of the full moon, the calm silvery surface of the old millpond at the bottom of the Dingle belied the rapacious dramas played out in its murky depths. Among the stems of water lily and pondweed at the edge of the dam a monster pike waited and watched. Its body was as long as four flower heads of the reedmace that grew at the margin of the pond, and wider than the span of a man's hand. Some twenty years before, the predatory pike began life as a pikerell, whose young, dark green body was striped with contrasting vivid yellow bars resembling the submerged stems of rushes and weeds in the water. Such camouflage not only enabled it to stalk its prey unseen, but protected it from its cannibalistic parents.

As the pike grew larger on its diet of perch, roach and tench, it became more intrepid and ventured into clearer water. There it gradually lost its disruptive coloration, the yellow bars breaking up into spots all over its back and sides. In this its present livery it had no need for mimicry, for it was an arch-predator among all the fish in the pond. Besides fish, other animals living in and around the pond had fallen prey to the voracious pike. The young of dabchick, moorhen and duck had been dragged beneath the surface and devoured. Water vole, rat and water shrew too had succumbed to the lightning strike of its savage jaws. Even adult geese and swans had been attacked, and several times a weasel in pursuit of a water shrew had ended up in the pike's stomach.

From the crown of a pollard willow at the edge of the pond, Aethelbeorht looked out over the water towards the dam. There he could distinguish the silhouette of an animal similar in form to his own kind, but a great deal larger. The dog otter sat up on his hindlegs looking out over the pond and scenting the warm night air, in an attitude also typical of his close cousin the stoat. Though not so often encountered in the parish, otters had always been known in the valley, for they were attracted by the large stocks of fish to be found in the many millponds and fish ponds, as well as by the waterfowl these harboured. And, like their smaller relatives, otters were particularly partial to rabbits, which they hunted in the warrens during their long journeyings between watersheds. Sometimes they were caught in gin traps set for foxes. It is said that when plentiful they were eaten during Lent, since they were a somewhat fishy food, being grilled or roasted and served with parsley and a piquant sauce made from sorrel leaves. When in such demand, bounties were paid, even to small boys, for killing otters that frequented the Frome, which flowed through the Golden Valley on the far side of the high commons of Rodborough and Minchinhampton.

A great wanderer, the dog otter had emerged from the tidal waters of the Severn at Saul Warth the previous night and had swum up the Frome as far as Ryeford, where in Anglo-Saxon times the rye harvest was carried across its ford. He left the water at a brook that flowed into the river and followed its course, as generations of otters had done before, through the water meadows of King's Stanley, whose manor had been the ancient demesne of the Crown and held by Tovi before and after the Norman Conquest. Reaching the brook's spring source at the head of a combe below Pen Wood, he killed a rabbit and slept off his meal in a badger set before continuing his journey in the early hours of the next day.

A solitary tawny owl, on the lookout for young rabbits at the edge of Pen Wood, witnessed the large weasel with the long broad tail and curious lolloping gait climb the steep scarp slope of Selsley Common, taking advantage of the narrow, contour-like tracks that centuries of soil creep and grazing sheep had made. On the cattle-cropped plateau of the common a group of inquisitive heifers watched the otter bounding towards the ancient road that ran along the summit of Selsley Hill and which formed the western boundary of Woodchester. The otter crossed the road, squeezed under a five-bar gate in the drystone wall, and ran across the field once known as Carter's Ground towards Dark Wood. The field adjoined one called Great Long Moor, a name redolent of woodland that once stretched the length of the summit and known in the Anglo-Saxon charter of the parish as Long Ridge.

The otter made his way down through Dark Wood, close to its intersection with Dingle Wood, sometimes using the steep, worn paths made by badgers to reach the pasture beyond, where he could smell the springs at the head of the combe. Following the stream through the Dingle, he arrived at the site of the former header pond where he took a mallard duck unawares, which was roosting in the dense stand of great willowherb that favoured the marshy ground. Then he moved on to the lower pond where he killed another duck, which, after eating all except the wings, beak and feet, he slept off in the hollow trunk of a pollard willow, and there he stayed for the whole of the next day.

Aethelbeorht watched the otter drop on to all fours and run along the dam, his short legs holding his body barely clear of the ground, his longer hindlegs giving a high arch to the lower back. Clinging to the steep bank by his wide, flattened tail, or pole, scarred at the tapered end by the teeth of Sir Hugh Arbuthnot's otter hounds, who hunted on the Little Avon near the Berkeley kennels, he slid noiselessly into the water. Though he shared with the royal hunter and other members of the weasel tribe the same long lineage, the otter was supremely adapted to hunting in water. He swam across the pond, propelling himself forward by fish-like movements of his sinuous, streamlined trunk and muscular tail, which he used as a rudder, and assisted by his webbed feet. Only the top of his broad, low head showed above water, the small, prominent eyes and short ears placed high up with nostrils on top of the muzzle, just above the water line.

When out in the middle of the pond, the otter filled his voluminous lungs and dived, valves sealing the nostrils and a flap of skin and fringe of hairs closing each ear against entry of water. When submerged, air trapped between the fine hairs of the underfur made the pelt waterproof, and the coarse guard hairs of the outerfur lay flat to give least resistance to the water. With whiplash movements of his body and powerful tail, and using the splayed webbed toes of his fore- and hindfeet like paddles, he reached a depth equal to four times his own body length. Though his eyesight was good, below the moonlit upper layers the water became muddy, making it difficult to find his prey. But the long, stiff, sensory whiskers or vibrissae that sprouted from his muzzle like a moustache, and from his chin, face and elbows, enabled the water weasel to detect fish from the currents their movements set up. The same organs of touch were brought into play when the otter had to negotiate rivers in spate, like the Wye and Severn, whose beds were strewn with boulders or other obstacles that were difficult to see in the turbulent or turbid waters.

Aethelbeorht saw the otter surface without having caught a fish, and watched him swim towards the bank which his willow tree lookout overhung. In the shallower water, amongst tree roots and pondweed, perch swam in shoals or sheltered in the shadowy shallows. The fish had rich greenish-brown backs, shading to yellow and white on the belly, and their sides were crossed with broad, dark grey vertical stripes which camouflaged them against the vegetation. The handsome perch with the large spiky dorsal fin and other fins of vermilion was the one fish out of all the others in the pond that gave the best sport to the young angler, for it could be taken with the simplest of tackle and the lowly garden worm as bait.

The fish had spawned during April and May, laying large numbers of eggs in the form of strings of tiny beadlets, each covered with mucilage by which they adhered to one another and to submerged tree roots. But their bright appearance made them conspicuous to the waterfowl of the pond, who soon reduced the original quantity to a small amount every year, and of those that hatched and grew on the pond plankton and the larvae of alderfly and mayfly, a number were eaten by pike as well as taken by anglers' hooks.

On seeing the huge shape of the otter's head loom from behind a curtain of pondweed, the perch scattered, except for one large fish with one eye missing. As the otter's large, forward-pointing canines closed on the perch's slimy body, the rich colours of its mimicry suddenly paled in response to the stress of the attack, in the same way it had reacted on the several occasions it had been hooked. When only six months old the same fish had been caught by a young angler, who on removing the hook, accidentally gouged out the eye before returning the fish to the water. Since he was short of worms, the boy put the eye on the hook as bait, and almost immediately it was taken by the same fish, so voracious was the nature of the species.

Aethelbeorht watched the otter go ashore underneath the willow, holding the floundering fish firmly by his sharp-cusped teeth. He listened to the noise the otter made as he tore off pieces of flesh, avoiding the spiny dorsal fin, and ground them up between the flattened molars at the back of his jaws before swallowing, all the while holding the slippery carcass steady between his forepaws. But the young royal hunter was not aware that his mother was hunting for water voles along the top of the earth dam on the far side of the pond.

Largest of all the voles, the water vole, better known as the water rat, made its burrows in the dam and round the edge of the pond, and so rapidly was it able to excavate them that it had earned the name water mole. One adult male that had been forced to live away from the security of a waterside hole by the burgeoning summer population, sat up on his haunches grasping a severed length of cocksfoot grass stem between his forepaws. Unlike his greatest enemy, the predatory brown rat, which terrorised young water voles in their nests, the water vole had a timid demeanour, was uninquisitive and quite unratlike. His nose was broad, eyes set close on top of the head, and his short, rounded ears were thickly furred with a flap of skin that sealed off the ear canal when he was swimming.

The water vole stopped gnawing the nutty core of the grass stem and ran stiffly towards the source of the sound he had heard, stood still and pointed nervously with his quivering nose held upwards. He smelt the unmistakable scent of stoat, for he had encountered the same smell in a labyrinth of burrows through which another stoat had hunted several days before. The vole's glossy black guard hairs stood erect, those on his face bristled and his whiskers pointed forwards. His small myopic eyes stared unblinking and his ears were cocked. With a sudden burst of energy, he scurried along a well used surface run leading to the water's edge and leapt in with a loud 'plop', which warned all the other voles in the vicinity that a predator was around.

Gytha followed the scent trail of the water vole down to the water, and without hesitation dived in after it. Following in the wake of the vole, she swam with all the confidence of her potential prey, for she was no novice to water, having been introduced to it by her mother during her first summer. Since then she had hunted water voles and rats along the banks of the brook, many times entering the water in their pursuit. She had also taken moorhens and ducklings on other ponds by pulling them under the water in the same manner as an otter. And like her close cousin she had even caught fish, particularly during the past winter when warm-blooded prey was more difficult to obtain.

She swam after the water vole with a series of accelerating jerks, paddling strongly with the splayed toes of all four feet and holding her head and shoulders above water, while she held her tail erect. When she was within a few body lengths of the vole, he thrust his head into the water and dived, propelling himself downwards by kicking with his hindfeet. Suddenly the rotund, furry form of the vole on land had become a slender, streamlined swimmer, the air trapped in his thick fur giving it a silvery sheen, some escaping as a trail of tiny bubbles.

Gytha dived also, valves in her nostrils and ears closing against the entry of water. Ahead of her she saw the air bubbles and a cloud of silt rising from the bottom of the pond, for the water vole was scrabbling in the mud in an effort to hide his retreat. But Gytha could detect the vole by means of her vibrissae, which sensed turbulence set up by her fleeing prey. As she homed in on the vole, she felt a sudden tug on her tail, followed by a sensation of numbness across her rump. The giant pike had her in its jaws, seizing her with the erect and pointed teeth in its hooked lower jaw.

Gytha struggled to break free from the pike's grasp, but to no avail. Her body became spiked by the rows of slender but very sharp teeth arranged in bands along the roof of the pike's mouth, and the more she struggled the more the backward-pointing teeth lacerated and held her. Her futile gasps for air drew water into her bursting lungs, and she felt a sharp pain in the middle of her back as her spine cracked. Her last sensation was seeing the moonlit water reduced to a tiny window, and losing consciousness, she was drawn backwards along the pike's gullet, the teeth in the roof of its mouth lowering to allow the now quiet body of the little royal hunter to be swallowed.

Aethelbeorht returned to his den in the pollard willow and slept close to the partly eaten corpse of a moorhen he had caught at its roots among the reeds. An hour before sunrise, he left his night refuge and made his way round the edge of the pond. He stopped to investigate the remains of a mallard duck and discerned the strong smell of the otter, whose scent is said to linger longer than that of any other predator. As he ran along the top of the dam he detected the scent of another stoat, which he recognised as that of the yearling dog stoat who had taken over Aethelwald's domain. Each time he encountered the same scent mark he felt uneasy and threatened.

Aethelbeorht's brothers and sisters were already living independently of one another, for they each needed their own territories, which were to be found throughout the woods and warrens of the Dingle, among the meadows bordering the brook, and in the gardens of large houses in South Woodchester. The young royal hunter explored further along the dam and followed the scent trail of a water vole to the edge of the pond. He also recognised the scent of his mother, and he stood for a moment gazing into the murky water, oblivious of the fate that had befallen her, then sped on in search of fresh fields in the south of the parish.

Tigress from Orpheus pavement

XVII

The thirteen-year-old boy woke to the sound of Jim Hammond's clanging milk churns outside Larchgrove Cottage. He lay in bed thinking about his adventures of the past few days during his summer stay at Woodchester. The previous afternoon had been unbearably hot as he and his aunt pushed their large-wheeled bikes up the long steep road known as Culver Hill to Amberley and Minchinhampton. There on the common he had flown his model glider, which the thermals rising from the hillside had carried far. During one of the many times he had to retrieve it, he had taken by surprise a stoat that was basking in the sun on a thyme-covered nest mound of the yellow ant. He was enchanted by the sight of such a beautiful and elusive wild creature, and he wondered if it was the same animal he had seen in Dingle Wood a few days before.

Then he thought about his visit to see the inside of a Stone Age long barrow known both as Uley Bury Tumulus and Hetty Pegler's Tump. He and his aunt had cycled to Uley along the ancient ridgeway road that went over Selsley Common, where they stopped to look for fossil seashells in a disused quarry. Next he remembered the pieces of mosaic his friend had given him, which he had found among the spoil from the recent uncovering of the Roman pavement in the old parish churchyard.

The boy sat up and reached over to the marble washstand beside the bed to make sure the tiny tiles were still there. He picked them up and turned them over on the eiderdown. Looking at the six small cubic tesserae of red brick, grey and cream limestone and red sandstone, he began to imagine what the pavement would have looked like when it was the floor of the villa's grand hall or dining room. He wondered what kind of people had lived at the villa and what sort of countryside there would have been in Roman times. He put the tesserae back on the washstand and sank back into the feather-filled pillows and mattress, and soon he had fallen into a deep, dream-filled sleep.

In his dream the boy was flying in a glider high over the edge of the wold. He could hear the wind whistling round the cockpit and feel it buffeting the delicate craft as it wheeled in a wide circle, ascending on thermals like a soaring buzzard. He could see for miles around. To the north lay Gloucester, the Roman city of Glevum, and beyond it the hazy, undulating range of the Malvern Hills, where in their hill fort the Iron Age Dobunni had defended themselves against the legions of Vespasian. To the west, past the snaking Severn, stretched the Forest of Dean and the Cambrian mountains, the country of a tribe called the Silures.

At the southernmost extremity of the wold, though too distant and shrouded in heat haze to discern, lay the Roman city of Bath or Aquae Sulis, dedicated both to the Celtic goddess Sulis and the Roman goddess Minerva, where healing thermal springs bubbled up from deep down in the rocks. To the east, at the meeting of three great Roman roads (Ermin Way, Akerman Street and Fosse Way), lay Cirencester or Corinium Dobunnorum. Said to be founded by Vespasian, lieutenant of Emperor Claudius during his conquest of Britain, Corinium was in the former territory of the Dobunni tribe. As capital city of the province of Britannia Prima it was an important market town for the many villas and native farmsteads around and also a noted centre for the Roman craftsmen who created mosaics like the Woodchester pavement. In his dream the boy had been transported back to the time when the Roman villa had reached its prominence.

The wold's wooded escarpment was deeply cleft by four valleys along which rivers flowed into the Severn, the Sabrina of the Roman historian Tacitus. The summits of the limestone hills had long been cleared of woodland by Stone Age farmers, and some were surmounted by the great earthworks of the Dobunni. There were also the grass-covered mounds of Stone Age chambered long barrows and the round tumuli of Bronze Age people. Below the escarpment the fertile vale reached westwards to the Severn, a patchwork of small Celtic fields bounded by hedges and earth banks, or lynchets, and large tracts of woodland, water meadows and marsh.

The boy looked down on the huge hill fort of Uley Bury where the Romanised Celtic descendants of its builders still lived in thatched, timber round houses and where their livestock were afforded protection from predators within the ditch- and rampart-bounded enclosure. A short distance to the north-east of the hill fort, on top of another hill, he noticed a crowd of people congregating outside a Romano-Celtic temple. The temple was dedicated to the god Mercury, whose larger-than-life stone statue and other bronze effigies adorned this place of pagan worship, where goats, rams and cockerels were sacrificed. Even human offerings, including infants, had been made here. At the base of a stone altar decorated with the relief sculptures of Mercury and his cult creatures, the ram and the cock, an inscription told that one Lovernius, meaning 'fox' or 'son of the fox' because of his fox-like intelligence and cunning, willingly and deservedly paid his vow to Mercury.

Further along the ridgeway the boy recognised the pear-shaped long barrow he had visited with his aunt. It stood near the edge of the escarpment, its stone portal facing the rising sun and flanked by two curved drystone walls, which formed two sides of a small forecourt where elaborate funeral rites had been performed. The boy and his aunt had collected the key from a nearby cottage in Uley and had unlocked the small low door that was placed beneath a large lintel of limestone at the entrance to the tumulus. The inquisitive and intrepid boy had crept along the short passage into the heart of the dark dank tomb where the burial chambers lay.

Great limestone slabs set in the ground supported others to form a roof over the drystone burial chambers, which the boy was disappointed to find had been blocked off. He had learned that almost one hundred years ago twenty-eight skeletons had been found in the five burial chambers along with the jaws and the perforated tusk of a wild boar. During Roman times, two thousand years later, the barrow had been used as a burial place, for coins depicting the three sons of Emperor Constantine had been found with several of the skeletons. In the reign of Charles II a couple, Henry and Hester Pegler, farmed an acre of land that included the barrow, which was called Cold Harbour, since it was used as a cold store, and thereafter it became known as Hetty Pegler's Tump.

Looking northwards a short way along the ridgeway, the boy could distinguish another long barrow, which he realised must be the one at Nympsfield, and which he knew as naked standing stones and drystone burial chambers without their roof of stone and soil. Soon he was spotting other barrows, each built by several tribal groups, for a great communal effort was required to transport the huge limestone slabs from a nearby quarry on Stone Hill and erect them, and to build the mound with hundreds of tons of limestone. But the boy was caught up in a reverie of a landscape more than two thousand years on from those first farmers, for he saw below him a wold and vale studded with Roman villas and farmsteads of the native Celts.

The boy glanced up through the cockpit of the glider to see a large brown bird with long broad wings circling on the thermals. The buzzard's outstretched wings, with upturned parted feathers, moved imperceptibly as they hung on the warm air currents, balanced by the fan-shaped tail. Soon he was close enough to see the barred feathers underneath, just like the feathers he had found in the Dingle, the head with yellow hooked bill and the penetrating, amber eyes. He was mesmerised by the bird.

Suddenly he felt the wind on his face, and he looked down to see the glider falling away below him. Then he knew he had become one with the buzzard. With an unimpeded view of the scene before him he scanned the land with the eyes of a hunting hawk, which can see over a wide field and at the same time bring distant objects into near focus. With this faculty the boy was able to discover the many secrets of the wold in Roman times. He could identify the steep, winding road that left the ridgeway midway between the two long barrows to descend the wooded escarpment into the vale. Leaving the Fosse Way in the east, which linked Corinium with Aquae Sulis, the stony rutted road crossed the windswept wold to join the ridgeway halfway between Uley and Woodchester. Half a mile from the foot of the escarpment it skirted several villas before traversing the vale to meet the Roman road heading south from Glevum, and then followed the Frome to the Severn.

The boy spotted one of the villas nestling in the vale. Somehow he thought, the half-timbered villa house with courtyard and Cotswold stone outbuildings, roofed with red sandstone tiles, looked strangely familiar, for he had visited the Elizabethan court and medieval tithe barn at the farm in Frocester. He had seen inside the ancient tithe barn, built with stone robbed from earlier buildings and whose huge oak roof timbers, replacing the original ones after a fire in the sixteenth century, supported the same kind of heavy tiles. Surrounding the villa house he saw most vividly other sights that he was more familiar with on the farms of Woodchester and neighbouring parishes.

There were open-fronted barns serving as cattle byres with enclosures of drystone walling. In one stood a solitary, large shorthorn bull with a bronze ring through its nose. The animal seemed to bear a remarkable likeness to Farmer Gibbs' bull at

Waterlane Farm, or the one from Fawkes' farm that was kept at times in the red-brick barn with the drystone wall enclosure at the corner of Oxlease. Other pens contained goats and sheep, and there were sties for white long-backed pigs as fat as the one the boy's grandmother kept in a sty.

There were neatly thatched round ricks of hay and straw, wood piles, wagons, and the usual untidy assortment of farm implements, from ploughs and harrows to scythes and pitchforks. Most familiar of all were the chickens, ducks and geese that roamed freely round the farmyard, the orchards of apple, pear and plum, and kitchen garden for vegetables, herbs and flowers. Even though he had never seen a real vineyard, the boy knew that the rows of trailing plants supported by what looked like a fence of willow must be grapevines. There were coppices of hazel and ash where the trees were cut to promote the growth of slender stems for hurdle-making, frameworks for wattle and daub walling, and handles for all manner of tools. And along the streams and ditches that ran through water-meadows grew willows that were pollarded for their strong, straight and flexible branches.

On the edge of the wooded escarpment, the boy saw a quarry in a clearing. Instead of the overgrown, disused quarry he knew, where he and his friends looked for fossils, lit camp fires and smoked, till they were nauseous, the woody stems of blithytwine that hung liana-like from the trees, he saw a place of industry. Men wielding long iron crowbars, hammers and wedges, removed blocks of creamy limestone from the quarry face and loaded them by means of a timber tripod and block and tackle on to a wagon drawn by a team of four oxen.

Though the oxen were an unfamiliar sight to the boy, the four-wheeled wooden wagon they were pulling seemed to be similar to the kind used on Fawkes' farm. Even the wheels were the same, for the felloe consisted of segments of bent ash fixed to an elm hub with turned spokes of willow, all held together by a shrunk-on iron tyre. The stone was destined for the villa, where an extension was being built to house an elaborate bath suite.

This was to comprise a heated dressing room, or apodyterium, a frigidarium with cold plunge, a tepidarium and a caldarium with hot bath. A boiler house, or praefurnium, would heat the water as well as the air that circulated in pottery wall flues and beneath the floors of those rooms with a hypocaust.

On the stout stone foundations masons had built walls of limestone cemented with lime mortar. The lime had been produced by burning limestone chippings in kilns and slaking the crushed powder in a shallow, clay-lined pit of water. Sand for the mortar was dug from the same pit at the foot of the escarpment that the clay for bricks, flues and tiles came from. Plasterers coated the exterior walls with a mixture of lime mortar and brick dust, and on the inside they plastered over wattle linings that carpenters had made from coppiced hazel. Wattle and daub was also used for internal partition walls.

Carpenters also erected the roof timbers, which they had sawn on-site from trunks of oak supported on a trestle over a saw pit. Across the rafters wooden laths were nailed to hold the heavy roofing tiles of local red sandstone. Tilers split and dressed the slabs of hard, durable sandstone to form hexagonal tiles with chamfered edges, and drilled a nail hole off the centre line of each. They secured the tiles point downwards to the laths with iron nails, and the position of the nail hole ensured that should a tile slip, the gap between the tiles in the row below would not expose a nail directly to the rain.

Along the vale road the boy saw a convoy of wagons carrying building and other raw materials for the villa. One was loaded with red sandstone, quarried along the banks of the Avon, which would be used for roof tiles, lintels, doorsteps, floor flags and water cisterns. In another wagon, which had crossed the Severn, were pigs of iron that had been smelted from ore mined in the Forest of Dean, coal to fire forges, and chunks of red and yellow ochre and other iron minerals for making pigments to decorate plaster walls and ceilings. A third wagon had travelled from Glevum with sheets, rods and tubes of bronze, which had been smelted from Shropshire copper and Cornish tin. Smiths at the villa would fashion the metal into brooches, bracelets, pins and pendants and a myriad of domestic tools and utensils, which were traded with the inhabitants of Uley and those living in the hill fort of Lydney with its great temple of Nodens, on the edge of the Forest.

Suddenly the boy felt himself being carried higher by the thermals, and northwards along the wooded ridgeway. Below him lay a steep-sided, thickly wooded valley. Could this, he wondered, be the ancient Woodchester Park, the forbidden place that his friends had dared to explore and where an unfinished mansion stood, which was said to be haunted? But he could see no such mansion, for the valley was still part of the great Roman estate whose boundaries stretched far beyond the bounds of the parish of Woodchester that he knew.

On the summit of the hill above the northern side of the valley the boy saw yet another Stone Age long barrow, and near it the round grassy mound of a Bronze Age tumulus. With his hawk-like telescopic vision he could even distinguish the wild flowers growing amongst the grasses of both burial mounds – lavender-blue scabious, mauve knapweeds and yellow horseshoe vetch. Close by the ancient tribal tombs stood the tenant farmsteads of the native Celts with their small fields enclosed by drystone walls. In some of the fields grew flax, with its powder-blue flowers fully opened to the sun, turnips, beans and other winter livestock feed. In others, ripened barley, oats and wheat were ready to be cut or stood as stooks of sheaves drying in the sun, long-horned sheep and shorthorn cattle grazed, and in a palisaded woodland clearing dark-skinned, long-legged pigs foraged, like their close cousins which the Celts both hunted and revered.

As the boy sailed on the thermals yet further northwards, he began to recognise the wooded combe that he knew so well as the Dingle. But, instead of woods mainly of lofty beeches, he saw managed coppices, and some of the small fields were under cultivation by serfs working on the estate. In one field of pasture he saw a figure cutting the lower branches from a lofty elm, which he threw down for the cattle to eat. He had seen George Fawkes doing the same thing during a summer drought when grass was in short supply.

On the steep hillside, where his aunt's cottage stood, the boy saw a mixture of stone, wooden and half-timbered houses with thatched and tiled roofs, set in small plots for growing food and keeping livestock. There was no parish church with great steeple nor the village school he had so reluctantly attended during his wartime stay at Woodchester. Along the valley bottom, water meadows stretched down to a wide stream fringed with pollarded alders and willows and dense stands of meadowsweet, willowherb, purple loosestrife, comfrey and hemp agrimony. He even fancied he could smell the heavy-scented flowers of the luxuriant waterside vegetation.

There was another familiar smell too that reminded him of his aunt's log fire. On the opposite side of the valley a column of smoke rose from a tall chimney where Workman's steam-powered sawmills should have been. But instead of great piles of beech trunks and sawn logs, there were stacks of bricks and tiles in the yard. On the hillside above the works he saw the clay pit that supplied clay for the Roman brickworks, and he realised it was in the same place as the fish pond he and his friends had fished in.

He saw too the coppiced woodland that supplied fuel to fire the kilns. The sight of a horse-drawn wagon carrying poles of beech and ash down the hillside seemed as familiar to him as Workman's shire horses drawing felled beech trunks from Dark Wood in winter. A tunic-clad figure, wearing hobnailed leather shoes decorated with punchwork, rolled out ochre-coloured clay and pressed it into wooden moulds to produce the same thin, square, red bricks the boy had seen incorporated into the remains of the old parish church. On the surface of one of the unbaked bricks laid out to dry in the sun, he saw the indented pattern made by the studded sole of the brickmaker's close-fitting shoe, or calceus, and he was reminded of the brick tile bearing part of a similar imprint that was found at the villa during a past excavation and which he had seen in the museum at Gloucester.

In the same field as the brickworks a road wound up the wooded hillside, which the boy identified as the one he often climbed to reach Amberley Common. This was the Roman road to Cirencester, the Roman capital, which traversed a huge, refortified, Iron Age hill fort, where descendants of the Dobunni lived in round houses. The road crossed the stream close to the brickworks and passed through Woodchester as part of the ancient way to Glevum. Along this road a team of oxen hauled a large four-wheeled wagon laden with wheat sheaves destined for the villa.

The boy saw the palatial villa nestling in the bottom of the sunlit valley, close to the stream he knew as the brook, and sheltered from the cold north and east winds by the steep scarp of the wold, of which Rodborough Hill was a part. The villa's buildings, mostly half-timbered with walls rendered in red plaster and roofed in red terracotta pantiles, which were similar to those that covered the red-brick barn in Oxlease, were arranged around three courtyards. The villa stretched from where the Old Priory would have stood to beyond what he knew as Villa Field, where the old oaks provided nest holes for jackdaws.

On the north and east there were kitchen and pleasure gardens whose vegetable plots, herb and flower beds and lawns, divided by limestone gravel paths, seemed as familiar as the grounds of Larchgrove where the boy's uncle was gardener. And he was sure that the short stout figure pushing an elmwood wheelbarrow was his Uncle Ernest. Along one side of the high drystone wall that enclosed the kitchen garden, the boy saw what he recognised as a line of straw beehives standing on raised platforms of Cotswold stone, and a beekeeper, wearing a protective veil of the finest muslin, bending over one of them. The beekeeper had removed the thatched, conical roof of the hive and was harvesting the golden honeycomb, which contained honey the bees had made from the nectar of meadowsweet, purple loosestrife, great willowherb and hemp agrimony that grew on the marshy ground alongside the stream at the height of the summer honey flow.

To the east of the villa, where the ground sloped down to the stream, sheep grazed the aftermath of a meadow that had recently been cut for hay. The hillside behind the villa looked particularly familiar, for here was an orchard just like the one from which the boy and his naturalist friends scrumped tart but juicy cider apples and pears at the end of the summer holidays. To the west of the villa he saw the fields he knew as Shortcombe and Oxlease, with Watery Lane winding between their hedgerows. In Shortcombe there were even haystacks like the ones he remembered.

Along the top of Oxlease a team of oxen was drawing a large wagon loaded with timber. As it approached the gate on to the lane, he noticed the wagon suddenly tip to one side and shed its load, and he remembered the time when Workman's team of four were drawing timber from Dark Wood. At the same spot the cart had shed a wheel and the axle had dug deep into the ground exposing a section of the underground Roman conduit that carried water from a spring below Dark Wood to the villa. He remembered seeing one of the limestone blocks with the water channel cut into it, which were joined together with clay and covered with slabs of limestone, and he had watched Lance Cordwell skilfully repair the channel so that it once more carried water to feed the fountain in the garden of the Old Priory. Lance was a local builder who was knowledgeable about the aqueduct. He had installed several inspection covers along its length so that he could check whether the channel had become blocked with debris.

Now the boy's gaze became fixed on the wagon of corn as it approached the outer courtyard of the villa along the uphill, cobbled driveway. Suddenly, he lost all sensation of floating and felt himself falling rapidly through the air, landing on top of the load of barley sheaves, where he was greeted by two boys dressed in the same kind of linen tunic and leather shoes he had seen the brickmaker wearing. Despite their unusual dress, the boy immediately recognised them as his naturalist friends, with whom he helped at harvest time. But instead of the well-known local speech, he heard a strange language like that which his Latin master often used to address the class at grammar school, and he found himself responding as fluently as if Latin was his mother tongue. The figure leading the ox team turned his head and looked up at him, and he recognised George Fawkes, the cowman from Fawkes' farm.

The wagon arrived at the large outer courtyard, on two sides of which were familiar-looking barns built of the same stone as the barn he knew that stood at the edge of Villa Field. Into the largest of these, whose doorway was taller and wider than the load of barley, the wagon reversed, the oxen responding reluctantly to the farmhand's commands. Then the boy found himself and his two friends throwing off the sheaves with pitchforks on to the bricked floor, as he had often done at threshing time. But instead of feeding a noisy threshing machine, the sheaves were picked up by serfs who stacked them ready for threshing with wooden flails.

Now the boy was walking with his friends through a wide monumental gateway, with a high arch supported by Doric columns, which led to the central courtyard. Inside the gravel-covered courtyard he saw a bustle of activity. A muscular blacksmith worked at a stone-built forge fired by Forest of Dean coal. Two farmhands herded cows into their stalls ready for milking, others were unloading sacks of barley from a cart and carrying them into the malthouse on the opposite side of the yard, while others were replenishing the granary with wheat from the corn drier. The boy experienced all the smells he was familiar with at Fawkes' farm, including the sickly sweet smell coming from the malthouse, like that which came from the brewery at Stroud when the wind was in the right direction.

The boy's friends called to him from the ornate, arched doorway to the cloister on the east side of the forecourt, and he followed them along the hypocaust-heated corridor, pausing frequently to marvel at the mosaic floor and the plaster walls richly painted with frescoes. Through the open door of one of the rooms that led off from the cloister he saw the house servants preparing food, and a tall woman who seemed to be in charge bore a striking resemblance to his aunt. Through another doorway he saw a room, with a mosaic floor and walls of coloured marbles, in which were low couches and stools upholstered in leather, wicker chairs, and a table with a marble top on which stood a porphyry vase of fragrant roses. And in every alcove there was a statue of some classical figure in white Carrara marble or oriental alabaster.

The boy turned a corner and saw ahead of him a crowd of people, adults and children, who appeared to be waiting in a queue. They were dressed in gaily coloured togas and tunics fastened together with bronze or pewter brooches and clasps, some inlaid with brightly coloured enamels, and on their feet they all wore hobnailed sandals or shoes laced with leather thongs that sometimes covered the calf. A few of the more elegantly dressed wore gold torques around their necks. In some of the faces the boy saw the likeness of people he knew from the village, and he realised that he had also seen them at the recent uncovering of the Roman pavement, where his aunt had been selling some of her famous cakes at the refreshments stall.

The crowd moved slowly forward until the boy stood at the main entrance to a huge, sunlit, square room which looked like a hall. It had a high, fan-vaulted ceiling, painted in repeated patterns of roundels, octagons and squares, supported almost halfway to the middle by four columns of simulated marble. The walls were decorated in multicoloured roundels, sprawling spirals and floral shapes and partly inlaid with pink- and green-veined Pyrenean marble. In several niches stood bronze and stone statues, including the marble figures of Cupid and Psyche in an embrace, and Diana Luna holding a flaming torch and with a sacrificial bull at her feet. At the centre of each wall stood an arched doorway of coloured, inlaid marbles leading to a corridor and other rooms.

But it was the sight of the great pavement itself which enchanted the boy most of all. He stood with his friends on the outermost border of the mosaic, which consisted of the Greek key ornament edged by a block chain and a band of red-brick tesserae.

Along with guests from Frocester, Kingscote, Chedworth, Ifold, Cherington, Stancombe and other villas in the neighbourhood who had been invited to the opening of the pavement, the boy listened to the wealthy villa owner, whose ancestors were Dobunni chieftains who once lived on Rodborough and who founded an earlier villa at Woodchester several centuries before. Standing near the middle of the pavement, dressed in a gold-trimmed white toga, the owner not only looked like, but had the same military bearing as, Commander Metcalfe of the Old Priory. The boy heard how he had commissioned the mosaicists of Corinium to design and lay the mosaic, and how it was dedicated to the legend of Orpheus who charmed all living things, as well as causing inanimate mountains and rocks to move and rivers to stop in their courses, by his singing and playing on the lyre. The boy was as engrossed as he would have been during a classics lesson at grammar school.

In the centre of the pavement a stylised sun symbolising Apollo, the god of music and reputed sire of Orpheus, was encircled by swimming fishes and crustaceans of river and sea on a background of white Carrara marble tesserae. These were bordered by an octagonal frame of twisted red and white braid. The lowest side of the octagon was left open so as to make room for the head of Orpheus, so suggesting that the fishes and crustaceans could hear him as well as the procession of birds – finches, doves, ducks, fowls, peacocks, partridges and pheasants, all interspersed with leafy sprays, which occupied the next compartment.

Orpheus, dressed in peaked Phrygian cap, striped tunic and leggings, was shown in a sitting attitude, facing the southern main entrance to the room, the lyre resting on his left knee, while his right hand plucked the strings. To his right his shepherd's cloak blew out behind him in the breeze, though without alarming the unmusical peacock, with its reputation for malice and pride, which approached him from that side. On his left the procession ended with a fox, noted for its guile and cunning. This circle was enclosed by a frame of bay leaves, three deep, resembling a large bangle, between the ends of which a space was occupied by the legs of Orpheus. Next to this there was a complete band of guilloche in red, white and yellow tesserae on which Orpheus' buskined feet rested, and between this and another identical band, upon a white ground, came the famous procession of animals.

The boy stood by the bearded mask of Neptune, which had lobster claws sprouting from the top of its head and from its ears a great acanthus roll, which encircled the animal procession. Walking in a clockwise direction, he identified the animals, each separated by a tree or spray of foliage, beginning with the maned lion below Orpheus' right foot. Next walked a lioness, preceded in turn by a wild boar, wild ass, elephant, wild bull, griffon, bear, leopard, stag and tigress. He was sure he had counted only eleven animals, not the twelve he and everyone else had been told existed at the recent opening of the pavement. And, as his aunt called him from the bottom of the stairs, in that transient state between sleeping and waking, he wondered if he had miscounted.

Woodchester Mansion

XVIII

From Rodborough to Minchinhampton, the windows of houses studding the hillside blazed in the light of the early evening September sun. But those of the derelict Victorian mansion that stood at the head of the steep, wooded valley known as Woodchester Park had no such glow, for the Gothic-style building had been abandoned before most of the windows of finely carved local freestone could be glazed. The builder of the mansion, wealthy merchant William Leigh, was a devout convert to the Catholic faith who had planned to live a self-sufficient, monastic and medieval life in Woodchester, which was reflected in the provision of a bakery, brewery, dairy, laundry and chapel. But in order to complete another of his ventures, the Woodchester Convent, the masons had to abandon their work on the mansion, leaving behind their scaffolding and a thirty-foot wooden ladder propped up against the wall. Since that time, almost one hundred years ago, the mansion had stood unfinished. Some say that mysterious, even ghostly, happenings caused the desertion.

The stone mansion stood on the site of a former Georgian one that had been owned by the Ducie family. Sir Robert Ducie, lord of the manor, had acquired a mansion in the Tudor style from Sir George Huntley, who had been granted the manor by Elizabeth I. Sir George had sold the original Woodchester manor in the north of the parish, which included the Norman church and manor house, built by the Maltravers family from the remains of the Roman villa, and had enclosed the valley with a drystone wall where he kept deer, rabbits, wild boar and fish. Later, the Earl Ducie dammed the stream that ran through the valley to form a series of six large ponds, and called his estate Spring Park on account of the many springs that fed the ponds.

As the sun sank below Frocester Hill flocks of jackdaws, woodpigeons and stock doves returned from their rich feeding grounds in the park to the security of the deserted mansion. They flew through the topmost windows to take up their regular roosts in the floorless rooms, on ledges and in niches where joists would have rested, on arches and corbels projecting from the unplastered stone and brick walls, on carved mantelpieces and on the oak roof timbers fifty feet above. A pair of kestrels called to one another from their perches, each a gargoyle of a hideous hound carved from local freestone, which jutted from the top of a buttress below the stone gutter, and through whose gaping mouth rainwater poured after the recent shower. The kestrels had reared four young in a nest in the clock tower and had fed them on some of the young pigeons that also nested in the mansion.

But most of all it was for horseshoe bats and other species that the mansion had become a summer sanctuary. Over the decades, each spring they left their winter quarters in Mendip caves and underground stone workings for the roof spaces of the mansion to have their young. Just before the sun had set over the Forest of Dean, greater and lesser horseshoes began to stir at their roosts under the roof of the brewery. Adult females and their single young hung close together from the wooden laths and edges of the Cotswold stone tiles by the delicate, hooked claws of their hindfeet, their dark brown, membranous wings folded against the sides of their bodies, which were covered with thick, fine and silky fur, smoke-grey with a tawny tinge on the back and yellow-white on the front. Some hung by one foot, and after moistening the claws of the other in their mouths, they groomed their soft fur with rapid scratching movements. They also stretched themselves, yawned to show their needle-sharp teeth, and went into all manner of contortions to lick clean their wings with their long tongues, and all the while making their low frequency chatter. Then, as dusk fell, the bats left their roost, a few at a time, mothers followed by their young, and flew between the louvres of the brewery ventilation chimney to their hunting grounds. Each small group of bats was well out of sight before the next sortie left the chimney, but all followed the same flight path over the roofs and central courtyard of the mansion to the meadow on the southern side, where they went their own regular ways, using their tiny eyes to find their favourite feeding areas.

From late spring to early summer the bats had spent most of their hunting time in woodland up and down the valley. Here, where it was warmer at night than in the surrounding parkland pasture, they found many moths, flies and beetles. Cockchafer beetles were their favourite, which they caught among the trees. The beetles had emerged from the surrounding pasture, where their larvae fed on grass roots, and had flown to the trees to mate. In July and August, when the breeding females were suckling their young, they had spent most of their time hunting over meadow and parkland where vast numbers of nocturnal moths, ground and dung beetles were hatching out. Now, as autumn approached, adults and young hunted together for fat dor beetles that emerged from their nests deep beneath cowpats. They also preyed on caddis flies and beetles that hatched from the ponds. Each evening most insects were active for the first few hours after sunset and just before dawn, so it was at these times that the bats were hunting.

Bounding over the meadow at the edge of Leaze Wood, Aethelbeorht watched the bats hawking low over the ground with their slow, fluttering flight, alternating with short glides. He heard the low frequency contact calls between mother and young and even the ultrasonic sounds emitted through the trumpet-like nostrils in the centre of the horseshoe-shaped nasal membrane that gave the bat its name. The nose-leaf concentrated the beam of sounds that bounced off the large ears, enabling the bat to home in on and capture its prey. He watched one of the bats swoop down on a dor beetle that was crawling over a crusty cowpat and take it in its wide open jaws, and he saw it land on a tree trunk, turning a somersault to grip the bark. He heard the crunching sound its teeth made as they bit through the tough skin of the beetle, removing the glossy, purple-tinged wing cases, head and legs to get at the soft body beneath.

A short while before the bats had stirred from their roost, Aethelbeorht had woken from his sleep in a den he had made inside the chimney leading from the fireplace of the servants' hall in the mansion. The den was filled with the debris of old jackdaws' nests and was thickly lined with the feathers of woodpigeons and stock doves that he had killed in their nests. During his month's stay in the valley he had lived well on a varied diet of rabbits, voles and waterfowl, for the ponds supported a plentiful supply of mallard, moorhen and little grebe. Once, when hunting round the edge of Honeywell Pond, he had nearly fallen prey to a heron as it stood statuesque in the cover of the reeds, its dagger-like bill ready to stab at passing fish or any small creature that came within its range. During its long residence in the park, the old heron had killed, besides water voles, several stoats and weasels that had been hunting for waterbirds, and even fish and frogs.

Aethelbeorht resumed his patrol along the edge of Leaze Wood, occasionally stopping to smell scent marks left by other stoats and to leave his own on stones that had fallen from the broken-down drystone wall. He crouched low in the grass to watch the pale form of a barn owl quartering the meadow. The owl was one of five which had been reared by a pair that had nested in the mansion. Now only three survived, for one had been killed by a tawny owl and the other by a stoat. The dog stoat had been hunting in the meadow one night when the owl swooped down on it and tried to carry it off, but the struggling stoat managed to bite deeply into the owl's breast muscles, and both predator and prey had fallen to earth mortally wounded.

Through the darkness of the wood Aethelbeorht saw the black and white mask of a badger as it rooted in the leaf litter for ground beetles, and he passed close to another snuffling in the grass for earthworms and turning over dried cowpats with its long front claws to find fat dor beetles. Despite its large size, and unlike its small cousin the stoat, the badger didn't rely on warm, bloody flesh for food. The fertile valley provided everything its plentiful badgers needed, from succulent bluebell bulbs and cuckoo pint tubers to beechnuts and acorns, and from slugs, earthworms, bumblebees and wasps to frogs, rats, mice and voles, young rabbits and the afterbirth of cows and sheep.

Aethelbeorht searched beneath a thicket of yew and laurel that grew amongst elm, beech, ash and oak at the edge of Leaze Wood, and which had been planted as part of the park's pleasure grounds. A yellow-necked mouse sat on the trunk of a fallen yew, gnawing through the woody stone of a yew berry to reach the nutritious kernel inside, and watched with its large, bulbous eyes as the stoat hunted below. Like its slightly smaller close cousin, the common wood mouse, the yellow-necked mouse used the tangle of horizontal and inclined branches to move around its territory more quietly than over the litter of the woodland floor. In this way it was less easily detected by the ultrasensitive ears of the tawny owl, its main predator in the valley. It could also outwit the agile tree-climbing stoat, which had been one of its enemies in Woodchester's ancient woodland since long before its first charter, except when it was hunted to its summer sanctuary in a tree hole.

Quenching his thirst at a stream that flowed into Middle Pond, and which issued as a spring high on the hillside between Stoneshard Wood and Pontin's Plantation, Aethelbeorht lifted his head in the direction of the loud, high-pitched cries coming from Break-heart-hill Wood on the opposite side of the valley. Here, outside one of the wood's extensive ancient sets, a large, six-year-old male badger was fighting with a two-year-old boar from another social group in adjoining Colepark Wood. The younger animal had attempted to couple with the same sow which the old dominant male had mated with over the last month.

The two boars chased one another over the great mounds of spoil outside the set's entrances and blundered through the undergrowth, striking out with slashing front claws and gnashing teeth, piercing the peace of the night with their blood-curdling yelps and screams, and filling the air with pungent musk in their excitement. The badgers' cries didn't alarm the royal hunter, or any other nocturnal creature that was abroad in the valley, except the two juvenile badgers born that year, which looked on with their mother, who carried two more latent lives in her belly. But the wise couple who lived in the stone house called the Cottage, above Leaze Wood, knew well the meaning of the badgers' cries at this time of the year.

Four hours after the old injured badger had returned to his set in Colepark Wood to lick his wounds, and two since the last horseshoe bats had gone to their roost in the empty mansion, Aethelbeorht woke to the warmth of the rising sun as its first rays reached the bottom of the deep valley. He looked out from one of his regular dens in a hollow elm that stood beside Honeywell Pond, the smallest of the park's six ponds, watching the mallard ducks, moorhens and little grebes. He spotted a fox eating the last of the season's blackberries, and after taking its fill, it began to gather bits of moulted wool that sheep had rubbed off on to the thorny stems. Aethelbeorht followed the fox's movements as it approached the pond, mobbed by a family of chattering magpies. He watched it enter the water backwards and slowly immerse itself until only the wad of wool it held in the front of its jaws showed above water. But Aethelbeorht couldn't see the fleas that had abandoned its pelt to take refuge in the wool that floated on the surface. He watched the wily old fox come ashore, shake itself vigorously, and trot off towards the wood, all the while being chivvied by the magpies.

Aethelbeorht began to feel pangs of hunger, for his stomach was empty again. Not every one of his hunting forays was a success, and he had to expend a good deal of energy patrolling his patch in the park and avoiding dominant adult dog stoats who had established territories there. Once he had a brief skirmish with a stoat of equal strength, and had escaped with no more than a torn ear. Also, he found hunting was fraught with danger from other, larger, four-footed predators that favoured the same kinds of prey. Yet the sight of the waterfowl on the pond heightened his longing for warm, bloody flesh, and he climbed down the elm tree to try his chances once more.

He prowled through the long grass at the edge of the pond, frequently stopping and raising his inquisitive head to look and listen and to scent the crisp September air. A scattering of brown feathers, downy ones from the breast, and stiff flight feathers whose shafts had been cleanly sheared, showed where the fox had killed a mallard duck while the royal hunter had been sleeping. Coming upon the feathers, Aethelbeorht smelled a familiar sickly sweet scent on them, and he felt the same kind of fear he had when he came across a similar scent on the headless corpse of one of his own kind outside a fox's earth in Marmontsflat Wood. A fox that was hunting for field voles in the rank grass of Fish Pool Ground, above Colepark Wood, had pounced on the stoat, biting it through the neck and shaking it like a rat.

Despite a certain sense of foreboding, Aethelbeorht was determined to satisfy his hunger, and sitting up on his hindlegs to make sure the way was clear, he galloped at full speed across open ground towards Colepark Wood, where he took cover in a bramble patch. For a while he lay down to rest, listening to the alarm cries of birds that had spotted him crossing the old deer park. Blackbird, mistle thrush, robin, dunnock, jay and magpie joined together to show their disdain for the royal hunter. Even a cock pheasant up in the wood gave his resonant 'korrk-korrk'. But Aethelbeorht was not perturbed by the shindy, and he bounded out from the brambles on to a track that skirted the wood, stopped to look about him, and hopped hesitantly back into cover. After several minutes he broke cover again, this time with more spring in his step, paused to glance at a blackbird that watched him from a safe distance along the track, and once more skipped back into the brambles.

Once again Aethelbeorht appeared on the track, but this time, instead of returning to cover, he began to perform the sorts of strange antics that the royal hunter sometimes resorts to in order to capture its prey. Such behaviour may be opportunistic and a means of conserving energy expended in hunting prey by pursuit or when scent is poor. He stopped several paces along the track, turned a somersault, and hopped a few more steps. Then, suddenly, he sprang straight up into the air, spinning his supple body in a corkscrew twist, and landed to roll over and over on the hard dry ground, catching his handsome jet black tail tip in his mouth as he went. Again he hopped back into the brambles, and again, after a short interval, he returned to perform his bizarre acrobatics, turning back as well as front somersaults, and alternating them with the same rapid body twists and rolls, scattering the first fallen leaves of autumn in his wake.

The blackbirds were now joined on the track by the same thrushes, robins and hedge sparrows that a short while before had proclaimed their distrust for the royal hunter. Even a family of diminutive whitethroats, or 'nettle-creepers', which had nested in one of the dense clumps of nettles that lined the track, peered down from their perches in the brambles to watch the stoat's curious gambols, uttering their scolding 'tacc-tacc' cries. The cock pheasant too had come down out of the wood to watch the spectacle more closely.

Uttering calls that were a mixture of curiosity and alarm, the feathered onlookers grew even more fearless and drew in closer to watch the uncanny act. Now Aethelbeorht became less energetic in his cajolery, behaving more as if he were wounded and distraught with pain, taking more time in between his twists and turns to view his audience, and at the same time getting ever more close to the nearest birds. The boldest of the blackbirds stood within a few somersaults and rolls of the royal hunter, flirting its tail and drooping its wings, and all the while giving out plaintive peeps. The cock pheasant grew even more inquisitive and approached with a series of short, agitated runs, and after each one it would stop and turn its head on one side to watch the royal hunter's frolics.

Aethelbeorht had both blackbird and pheasant firmly in his sights. He had made up his mind which one was to be his prey. Then, at the finish of a front somersault, he made a sudden side spring and jumped on to the pheasant's back, grasping it round the neck with his front paws and biting into the back of its thin skull with his sharp canines. The pheasant began to run along the track, flapping its wings, its loud screams carrying through the valley, while Aethelbeorht clung on tightly and buried his teeth deeper into the skull until they found the hind brain.

In a desperate attempt to rid itself of its captor, the pheasant finally became airborne. Yet Aethelbeorht hung on ever more tightly, tearing the shimmering, dark green feathers from its neck with his incisor teeth and ripping out the veins and throbbing arteries just below the surface of its skin with his canines. Now he began to feel the pheasant's strength ebbing. Its wingbeats became more laboured as its rapidly pumping heart forced out more blood from the severed vessels in its neck.

Then, suddenly, both predator and prey plunged to the ground. The pheasant lay on the woodland floor in its death throes, beating its wings feebly, honking hoarsely through punctured windpipe, and lashing out wildly with its scaly, spurred feet. Aethelbeorht lapped hungrily at the warm blood that flowed freely from the lacerated neck. With his canines he tore off more of the rich red muscles that clothed the vertebrae and sheared them into fragments with his carnassials before bolting them. Soon he was satiated and had recovered enough strength to drag the three-parts grown pheasant into an old rabbit stop in which a doe had given birth to her last litter three months before.

Gargoyle from Mansion

Southfield Mill House

XIX

Only a waller, who was repairing part of the drystone wall that ran alongside the main road from Stroud to Bath, witnessed the lithe bitch stoat cross over from Little Britain Farm and vanish through a drainage hole at the base of the wall. During the many years he had been plying his trade, the most ancient of all country crafts, the wise old waller had observed at first hand the ways of the elusive royal hunter and its smaller cousin. He was well versed in the habits of most wayside wildlife, and he took great pleasure in sharing his rare, intimate knowledge with the two young naturalists from the village. Some adults, though possessing a great deal more book learning, but less humility, than the waller, were often reluctant to believe some of the accounts of observations he had made, and they were the poorer for it.

Sometimes, when he was working on a wall that enclosed a wood or one of the small fields in the valley, he would see a bitch stoat carrying a young rabbit, bird or vole to her nest she had made in the wall. On one rare occasion, while repairing a wall the previous winter, he had come across the nest of a royal hunter made of grass and lined with sheep's wool and the dried skins of wood mice and voles. Another time, he found a cache consisting of the dead bodies of three wrens, a goldcrest and chaffinch, a wood mouse and a woodpigeon's head. In winter, especially, it was not unusual for him to find the headless corpses of lapwings sticking out, tail-first, from the walls surrounding the larger fields on the top of the wold.

He carefully selected another piece of stone from the pile and laid it edgeways alongside other toppers to hold the top course of the mortarless wall in place, and to keep out the rain. He had almost completed the restoration, and he hoped it would be a long time before he had to carry out another repair on the wall. He had no time for people who drove their cars recklessly. It seemed to him that during the six years since the end of the war there were more and more vehicles on the roads, and that not only were they damaging roadside walls but were killing and maiming more wildlife than he could ever remember. And he was saddened at the sight of the increasing amount of litter that was being thrown from cars and lorries to desecrate his beloved county. He was well aware too that some of the weekend visitors from the towns, with their new-found, post-war wealth, were even removing stone from broken walls to take back in their car boots for their garden rockeries.

Early the previous morning he had found a young dog fox on the roadside verge that had been hit by a car. Its slender back had been broken by the impact, and as he approached, it tried to escape, dragging its paralysed hindlegs behind it. Not wishing to prolong its suffering, he soon put the cowering creature out of its pain by giving it a smart blow across its skull with his stone dressing hammer. The fox had crossed over at the same spot as countless past generations of foxes had done, even long before a road had been built through the valley one hundred and seventy years before.

Over the years the waller had seen badgers, stoats, weasels, hedgehogs, and even an otter, run over, for it was the animals' instinct to cross the valley in the ancient footsteps of their ancestors. He had noted that some of the sow badgers and bitch stoats were pregnant or suckling young in the nest. He knew too that most of the stoats were so intent on following the scent of a rabbit that they had not been aware of vehicles passing along the increasingly industrialised valley. On one occasion he had seen a bitch stoat shepherding her family of six kittens across the road when she and three of her young were struck down by a car.

Once he had seen a large dog stoat and buck weasel locked together in mortal combat in the middle of the road, oblivious of such man-made dangers. And he would never forget the time last September when he was walking down a lane and a family party of stoats crossed his path. One of the stoats, which he supposed was the mother, suddenly jumped up at him and clung on to his coat-tail by her teeth, while the youngsters ran round him squeaking shrilly and tried to run up his legs, and although he managed to shake them off, they followed him some distance before relenting and running off into the grass verge.

Yet of all the sights he had seen while building or repairing drystone walls, none was so rare as the funeral of a royal hunter he had witnessed at the close of summer. He was working on a broken-down wall at the edge of Atcombe Wood in South Woodchester, when he saw a pack of stoats making their way between the trees. He counted nine animals moving through some fallen timber. They were performing their familiar, grotesque dances, some turning cartwheels, while others bobbed from side to side, and all the time they made high-pitched shrieks.

Three of the stoats were pushing along the ground what looked like a mass of twigs and dead leaves rolled into a ball, lifting it over fallen branches that lay in their path. As the odd procession approached the wall, the waller was able to watch their behaviour more closely. The stoats halted at an old rabbit hole, and he could see that beneath the woodland litter was the limp corpse of another stoat. He watched in disbelief as three of the stoats pushed their dead companion into the hole, while the rest of the party joined in to scrape loose earth and leaves into it until it was sealed. Then the stoats returned to the wood in a flurry of russet and white fur.

The waller remembered the old country folk tale that weasels held funerals, so why, he thought, shouldn't stoats do the same? After all, he knew that badgers sometimes buried their dead. He had read that weasel funerals had been recorded in Gaelic, Celtic and Norse literature, and that in such ancient times the weasel was regarded as a fairy animal or as the property of fairies, and was often credited with supernatural powers. At the time he thought he should keep this strange stoat encounter to himself, for fear of being ridiculed. Sometime after the event he related it to the young naturalists, and he was pleased that they believed him.

As he placed the last of the toppers on the wall, he heard the loud warning cries of a moorhen coming from the direction of the brook where it ran through an ancient water meadow on the other side of the railway, and he reckoned that the bitch stoat he had seen cross the road a few minutes before must be hunting there. The stoat was Aella, one of Aethelbeorht's two surviving sisters. She had spent the previous night in one of the corn ricks at Little Britain Farm, which stood on the site of the Roman brickworks, where she, along with several weasels, had reduced the numbers of mice and rats that infested the unthreshed corn.

Aella prowled through the lush grass on the bank of the brook, searching for the scent of water voles that burrowed along its length. Water voles abounded along the brook, especially among the old withy beds, where in spring they relished the succulent young shoots of willow. They were easy prey for stoat, weasel, otter and heron, and where the brook ran through water meadows they were taken by the barn owl. But it was that most voracious and carnivorous rodent, the alien brown rat, resident in the valley for only the last two hundred years, which was the vole's most feared enemy. The rat was tireless in its search for young voles in the nest, and besides chasing adults relentlessly along the banks of the brook, it would even pursue them through the water to their death.

Soon Aella came upon the trail of a water vole, which she followed to one of the three entrances to its burrow in the bank. As she entered the burrow she detected another familiar scent that masked the one she had been tracing, and she sensed it belonged to a rat. She followed the long, dark, winding passage, using her touch-sensitive vibrissae, until she came to the water vole's food store, which it had been accumulating in preparation for the winter. Next to the food store was the nest chamber, which the water vole had filled with dry grass blades, teased out grass roots and soft stalks of hay, gleaned from the meadow's summer harvest, all carefully woven into a round, roofed nest, and curled up inside slept a large buck rat, twice as large as the slightly built bitch stoat.

That same morning the rat had devoured one of the young water voles from a female's last litter of the season. Though living independently of their parents, the litter of three stayed within the territory of their parents, yet they were powerless in shielding their offspring from the crafty and aggressive brown rat. As Aella approached the nest, the rat stirred from his light slumber, and sniffed in the smell of the stoat through his twitching nostrils. His nose and long vibrissae quivered nervously, and the ruddy-brown hairs on his back bristled as he cringed, belly uppermost, in the nest, hissing and baring his long, orange, chisel-edged incisor teeth.

Aella was well aware of the danger confronting her, for she had already felt the bite of a rat she had cornered in a barn at Little Britain Farm. She drew back and waited her chance. She began to taunt the rat by nipping the end of his long, thick, scaly tail, which made him strike out at her and bare the vulnerable back of his neck. But, though in total darkness, each time the rat attacked, Aella's ultrasensitive whiskers and lightning speed enabled her to avoid his sharp, snapping teeth. As the angry rodent lunged at her once again, she dealt the death blow as swiftly as a snake, and held him behind one ear until his muscles had given their last tremor. After gorging herself on his blood and eating out his brain, she curled up alongside the cooling corpse and slept.

As the church clock chimed eleven, Aella woke from her short sleep, ate some more of the rat, and carefully groomed herself. With her incisor teeth and rough-coated tongue, she removed the tiny hooked fruits of enchanter's nightshade that lodged in her fur. She had picked up the ripe fruits from plants growing in a beech wood below Amberley. By attaching its fruits to the coats of passing woodland mammals the plant spread itself far and wide. It is said the Anglo-Saxons used this diminutive member of the willowherb family as a protection against elves, calling it aelfthone.

Aella followed the water vole burrow till she came out into the sunlight at the water's edge. She sniffed at the shiny black droppings which a male water vole had recently deposited on a willow branch that had fallen across the brook, and she ran across the partly submerged branch to the opposite bank. As she prowled through the long grass she was constantly on the alert for the sight and scent of the tomcat from nearby Southfield Mill House, which often hunted in the meadow and along the banks of the brook. Besides catching field voles, the large yellow Persian would sit outside the holes of water voles at the top of the bank waiting for them to emerge, in the same way that it would catch young rabbits leaving their nest holes. During the last week it had killed one of Aella's brothers. It had carried the stoat alive into the kitchen of Southfield Mill House, where it let it go before chasing and cornering it. The cook had witnessed the short but fierce struggle. Rolling over on to its back and holding the stoat at arms' length by the extended sickle-shaped claws of its powerful forepaws, the cat leaned over and gnawed the back of its muscular neck until it was dead. Only the week before the cat had brought in the headless body of a young bitch stoat from another litter born in the valley, having first bitten off the head and eaten it, since, like the stoat, it was particularly fond of the brain of its prey.

The cat was particularly adept at catching the tiniest of weasels which the waller knew as the miniver or 'the little furry one'. Known also as kane, vair or fairy, this pygmy weasel was thought to be distinct from and smaller than the ordinary female weasel. Though some naturalists doubted the existence of a dwarf race of weasel, the waller had it on good authority that it was a separate animal, since a keeper friend of his had known of an orchard on his beat that one year harboured two litters of stoats, one of weasels and one of vairies. Instead of the usual russet coat of the common weasel, the miniver wore a rather drab, chocolate or bluish-grey one. It also had a thinner, more pointed, head with scant whiskers, and a mole-like tail, though furred. The vairy was mainly a mouse hunter, and became easy prey for the cat, who pounced on it as it travelled along the labyrinthine grassy runs of field voles that permeated the water meadow.

As she patrolled the brook, Aella often scent-marked tree roots, sticks and stones to establish her territory and warn other females that frequented the same stretch of water. The territories of her only surviving sister, and a female born to the bitch stoat who had lost her forelegs in a gin trap, also encompassed meadowland and withy beds along the whole length of the brook. Each of the three small territories was contained within the larger one of the far-ranging yearling dog stoat who had supplanted the dead Aethelwald and who had impregnated Aella, her sister and other bitch stoats at the beginning of summer.

Aella squatted to leave her mark by the gate that led from the meadow, before darting across the footpath that ran alongside the grounds of Southfield Mill House. At their nursery window the children watched the beautiful stoat gallop round the lawn in tight circles, stop for a moment, and then tear round again. Aella cavorted with her back arched, rolled over and over, and ran in circles on her hindlegs, holding her forelegs out like a performing circus animal. Each time she stopped she looked towards the flower bed where several small birds had begun to congregate. She then ran into a clump of Michaelmas daisies, whose pollen and nectar were eagerly sought after by hoverflies and late-foraging honeybees.

The children saw Aella dash out from the daisies on to the edge of the lawn, chasing her tail round and round, faster and faster. Six pied wagtails, which had been reared in a nest hole in the bank of the brook, flew into the middle of the lawn and watched intently in a semicircle. Suddenly, Aella leapt into the air and turned a complete somersault, showing her white underparts. Six more wagtails from another nest joined the others. She ran into the flower border and rolled over some low-growing plants, constantly keeping the inquisitive birds in her sights. Then, as she darted out on to the lawn once more and began to dance more brilliantly, enticing the wagtails closer, the children opened the window and clapped loudly to frighten the stoat away, for they couldn't bear to see the tiny birds harmed.

That same evening, as the children slept, Aella climbed the wisteria that grew against the rear wall of the old Cotswold stone house and crawled under the eaves into the roof space. Against the warm chimney she had made a nest from the fur and feathers of prey she had caught along the brook, and she added to it the wings of a pied wagtail she had taken from its withy bed roost.

Teasel tower, South Woodchester

XX

A heavy overnight snowfall blanketed the village, muffling the three-quarter chimes of the church clock. Even the usual resounding cries of the rooster in the pound adjoining Larchgrove Cottage succumbed to the sound-deadening, white shroud. Up steep Selsley Road the icy wind had piled snow high against banks and drystone walls, and had carved from the drifts shapes like frozen breakers reminiscent of an Arctic landscape. Jim Hammond trudged in spiked boots, leading his snow nail–shod horse that drew the milk cart, whose wheel chains left braided patterns in the compacted snow. The chink of his churns, the squeal of the dry hinges on the iron gate, the ring of his ladle against the milk can, and the placing of the can on the slate doorstep were all dulled by the thick snow covering the rustic porch and the narrow, box-hedged, iron-fenced front garden of the cottage.

In her wash house, Lilian Cashmore emptied a saucepan of small potatoes she had cooked in her haybox into a bucket and mashed them, adding several measures of bran to make a warm feed for her hens. Then she carried the bucket of feed to the rainwater tank, where she filled a can with drinking water for the hens. As she trod the snow-bound path to the pound entrance, she noticed the tiny surface tracks and vents in the snow made by wood mice that had been drawn during the night to the pound for the titbits left by the hens the previous day. She could also distinguish the large, deep, clawed footprints of a badger leading from the hill to the pound gate. But she knew that even if Brock managed to dig his way under the gate, her hens would be safe in their lock-up shed with its high perching rails.

After she had fed and watered her fowls, she cleared the six-inch layer of snow from the bird table on the small lawn at the top of the garden, and on it she placed some of the bran and potato mash and pieces of ham fat. She also filled an old enamel pie dish with water for the birds that thronged to the table and which gave her so much pleasure to watch from her living room. Robins, dunnocks, titmice, chaffinches, blackbirds and thrushes, including winter migrants from Scandinavia, and even green and great spotted woodpeckers, nuthatches and jays were visitors to the table in the harsh winter weather.

Next, she carried down coal and beech logs from the store at the top of the garden to fuel the living room fire which, except for a paraffin heater in the kitchen, was the only source of heat in the cottage. After taking breakfast with her husband on his return from his work at Larchgrove, she took down from the wash house wall a pair of cobwebbed snowshoes, which resembled Edwardian tennis rackets, strapped them over her boots, and with all the confidence of a cross-country skier, she set off down the steep hill to the Piano Works to catch a bus for Stroud.

Over in the Dingle mixed flocks of fieldfares and redwings scoured the hedgerows for the last remaining berries, hips and haws. Over the last few months these winter visitors from the pine forests of Scandinavia, Russia and Siberia, had journeyed westwards across the wold where, joined by resident and immigrant mistle thrushes, they had foraged on stubble and pasture, and feasted on the fleshy fruits of hawthorn, holly, yew and dog rose, and, in the gardens of Woodchester and neighbouring parishes, the fruits of pyracantha, cotoneaster and snowberry. Weakened by their long journey from the north, some of the migrant thrushes were easy prey for sparrowhawks. Others succumbed to the cold and their wasted corpses became unexpected food for foxes, stoats and weasels.

In a crab apple tree growing in the hedgerow separating Coneygre from Bean Acre, two mistle thrushes noisily defended their bounty of berries from their migrant cousins, for the bare branches of the tree were clad in the lush green growth of mistletoe, whose succulent, white berries the mistle thrushes eagerly devoured. It was due to its likeness for the fruits and the consequent spread of the seeds of this part parasitic plant to other trees such as lime, oak, poplar and willow that the bird was once known as the mistletoe thrush.

In the alders that grew along the banks of the Dingle stream, gaily coloured redpolls and siskins, from nearer northern latitudes, performed their acrobatics to extract the nutritious seeds contained in the trees' woody cones, all the while carrying on their metallic twittering. A jay flew out of Dingle Wood to search for acorns that it had cached during the autumn. Despite the snowy landscape, the canny crow possessed a mental map of the trees at the edge of that part of the wood along which it had buried the acorns, so knew exactly where to dig through the snow and into the soil beneath to find its winter stores. Nearby a robin picked over the leaf litter scratched up by badgers foraging for beetle grubs during the night. It also kept an eye on a molehill erupting beneath the snow, for the earth-moving activities of the ever-active voracious mole often brought insect grubs and worms to the surface, in the same way that the digging of the gardener, that other ally of the robin, benefited the bird.

Suddenly, from the hedgerow there flew up a flock of fieldfares and redwings, calling out in alarm, as a low-flying sparrowhawk took one of their number by surprise. The hawk carried the squawking redwing in its talons to one of its feeding stations on a beech stump at the edge of Dark Wood. It held the still live bird against the stump – mottled breast, characteristic chestnut flanks and underwings uppermost – and tore the handsome head with the prominent buff eyestripe from its pulsating body and swallowed it. Then it began to pluck the feathers from its breast until it had exposed sufficient bare flesh to tear off in strips with its sharply hooked bill.

From a nearby branch a carrion crow watched the sparrowhawk feed. The crow was never far from a kill, whether it was made by hawk, fox or stoat. Yet, like these predators, the gore crow was as much a carnivore as a feeder on carrion, for often, with the help of others, it had killed rabbits that crowded the warrens of the Dingle at the height of the breeding season, first pecking out their eyes to hinder their escape. The crow had killed a partridge by pouncing on it from a hover a few feet above the ground and stabbing it in the back with its powerful black beak. While it was raising a brood, the cock bird and his mate had even brought down a woodpigeon. While his mate flew alongside the pigeon, cawing, he stooped at it like a falcon, buffeting it with his wings and trying to peck at it. Eventually, the pigeon was forced to the ground and killed by both crows. During the last week of snow the crow had despatched several redwings as they gorged themselves on the dwindling hedgerow harvest.

A local rabbit catcher, Sturdee Click, who regularly shot, ferreted and long-netted rabbits in the parish, trudged through the snow on the cart track that ran along the top end of Coneygre. Though christened Henry Edward, the rabbit catcher had always been better known as Sturdee, after Admiral of the Fleet, Sir Doveton Sturdee, victor of the Falkland's engagement during the Great War. Slung over one shoulder, Sturdee carried an oblong box in which he kept his ferret, and over the other a haversack containing purse nets, wooden pegs and two rabbits he had caught earlier that morning. As he walked he noticed the footprints of the various creatures that had defied the snow to find food during the night. The well-defined, deeply penetrating, clawed prints of heavy badgers told him that the animals had probably visited the gardens of houses on Selsley Hill, especially Larchgrove, where he knew the owners regularly put out food for them. Alongside these he saw the shallower and slimmer dog-like tracks of a fox set out in a straight trail. He noted that every fourth print lacked the impression of claws and pads, and he guessed that the trail belonged to the lame fox with one front paw missing that he had sometimes seen about the warren during the summer.

Sturdee also saw the many shallow trails of rabbits whose furry feet, especially the long hind ones, supported their weight like snowshoes, and running behind some of them were the unmistakable footprints of the royal hunter. These showed the five tiny toe pads and claws radiating from the lobed pads of the palm and sole of fore-and hindfoot. Since the tracks of the hindfeet were almost superimposed on those of the forefeet, and the length of the gap between each complete set of tracks was equal to that of the rabbit catcher's boot, he could tell that the stoat had been moving at a slow gallop. Like a true hunter, Sturdee was well versed in the art of animal tracking.

Some yards ahead a rabbit came out of a bury at the edge of the hedgerow. Its erratic gait told Sturdee that it was being pursued by a royal hunter. The human hunter crouched by the hedge and waited. After a few moments he saw a dog stoat follow the rabbit in laboured bounds over the snow to the middle of Coneygre. As the stoat drew nearer, the petrified rabbit lay down and allowed the stoat to overtake it. It uttered not a sound. Sturdee knew from long experience that here was an easy catch. He started to approach the rabbit, and got to within about ten yards before he was seen by the stoat, who dived beneath the snow. When he reached the rabbit it lay motionless, its eyes closed, as if dead. He gently picked it up and felt its heart palpitating violently through its limp body. He knew that if he didn't kill it, the large buck rabbit would probably suffer a lingering, painful death from the stoat, so holding it up by its hindlegs, he gave it a smart blow across the back of the neck with the outside edge of his outstretched hand, killing it instantly.

There was no sign of the stoat, but a long ridge of snow, like that of a mole-run on the surface of a meadow, showed where he was making his escape. About twenty yards distant Sturdee saw the inquisitive stoat put up his head, only to disappear again. And as he walked towards the spot to get a closer look at the royal hunter, he saw that he was burrowing rapidly along just below the surface of the snow, making for the bury from which he had bolted the rabbit, every ten yards or so putting his head up to check on the human hunter.

Sturdee approached the bury where he thought the stoat had gone to ground. He took great care to tread softly, for even with the deadening effect of the snow he knew that rabbits deep down in the burrows were sensitive to unfamiliar noises. The animals' fear of the unknown above ground often equalled their fear of the predatory ferret. Sturdee put down his ferret box and haversack on the snow and examined the entrances to the bury. Outside one of them he saw the tracks of the rabbit that had been bolted by the stoat. He also saw the tracks of the stoat and could tell by their direction that the animal had left and returned to this same hole. He took the purse nets from the haversack and pegged one across each of the entrances. Then he opened the lid of the box and took out his ferret, which was a female or Jill. The docile, cream-coloured cousin of the polecat blinked her pink eyes at the bright sun-reflecting snow, for they lacked the protective pigment of the wilder relative. For more than two thousand years ferrets had been used to hunt rabbits. They had been brought to Europe from North Africa, and had been used by the Spaniards to deal with their rabbit plague. In Woodchester they would have been used to bolt rabbits when man-made warrens became established.

Sturdee only ferreted in the depths of winter when the rabbits were well-grown adults and most of the does were not bearing

211

or suckling young. At other times he and Frank Bennet would catch them in large numbers by long-netting. The nets were run out at night, downwind from the rabbits, about fifteen yards from the wood, when the animals were out feeding. Then Sturdee and Frank, with the help of their fast dogs, would drive the rabbits into the slack bottom of the net and quickly despatch them by skilfully dislocating their necks as they became caught in the net.

Sturdee attached a line to the ferret's collar, and introduced the animal to one of the entrances through the mesh of the purse net, which was small enough to prevent the escape of even a young rabbit. The line was necessary in case the ferret failed to bolt her prey but killed it by biting through the spinal cord at the back of the neck, and so preferred to stay below ground to make a meal of it. At such times Sturdee had to dig out his ferret and the kill. He was able to judge the distance the ferret had travelled by the length of the knotted line that he had played out. And by putting his ear to the ground and listening for the thuds made by the dying rabbit's hindfeet thumping the sides of the burrow, he got a good idea of the location of the kill, and so was able to dig down vertically to retrieve both predator and prey. Although he had ensured his ferret was well-fed on rabbit flesh before he came out to hunt, he could not always be sure whether or not the smell of the living prey would rouse her deep-rooted instinct to kill.

The ferret scurried down the rabbit burrow on her short legs. She felt more secure in this dark underground world. Sturdee watched the marked line travel past the entrance and then suddenly stop. The ferret stood still, her tail and hindquarters quivering as she smelt the unusual occupant of the burrow. The dog stoat, curled up in the nest chamber of his prey, heard the snuffling sounds of his larger cousin, and smelt an overpowering odour wafting along the tunnel. The stoat, one of Aethelbeorht's two remaining brothers, had spent the first two months of winter hunting and lying up in the warrens of the Dingle, sometimes within earshot of a snoring fox or badger. But the ferret, like the once familiar polecat, was not a welcome bedfellow. Its fighting strength and biting power exceeded that of the stoat, who bore the recent scars of combat.

The previous month Sturdee was ferreting at the edge of Dark Wood, and wishing to have both hands free to remove some undergrowth, put down his ferret for a moment on a heap of dead leaves. Suddenly there was a flurry of reddish-brown and white fur, as a large dog stoat, which had apparently been disturbed from his sleep in the morning sun, fought with the ferret. Only after Sturdee intervened with his boot did the stoat depart from the scene with a bitten muzzle and torn ear, but not without inflicting similar wounds on the ferret. This time Aethelbeorht's brother was not stopping to wrestle with his superior cousin, and he bolted from another burrow, easily clearing the mesh of the purse net, and sped off towards Dark Wood, leaving behind him a pungent smell of musk.

Walking along the bottom of Dark Wood Sturdee observed other tracks of a dog stoat, which by their size he reckoned might belong to the same one his ferret had bolted. The animal was evidently in a hurry, for the tracks of the hindfeet were separate from but close to those of the forefeet, and there was almost a foot and a half between each set of tracks. And two shallow, parallel grooves in the snow showed where at each long bound the hindfeet had skimmed the surface. Then he noticed that the tracks joined up with the deeper tracks of a rabbit running alongside. Sturdee followed the trail for several hundred yards and saw that it began to zigzag, then run in circles, and presently the snow was scattered and trodden in a big patch.

From these signs in the snow Sturdee could deduce that the stoat had seized his victim and rolled it over. He guessed that the rabbit was no doubt a large buck the determined stoat had bolted from another bury, and it would not be an easy one to kill. Seemingly, the rabbit had recovered, for its tracks went on, though now less distinct and closer together. Also, the stoat had obviously left his prey, for a trail went away up into the wood for twenty yards or so. Perhaps, Sturdee thought, the royal hunter had caught wind of him or even seen him amongst the bare beeches of the wood. He reckoned he must be close to the enactment of a kill.

Sturdee stood still and scanned the steep, snow-clad floor of the wood some fifty yards ahead, and there he saw both royal hunter and large buck rabbit, several times the stoat's size, wrestling in the snow. Then he heard the heart-rending scream of the rabbit, which he had heard many times before, and which never failed to make the hairs bristle on the back of his neck or a chill to run down his spine. Despite his pains to remain silent and unnoticed by the stoat, Sturdee accidentally trod on a brittle beech branch, and although the tiny snap was muffled by the snow, the sound was sufficient to alarm the stoat, who streaked off across the snow and disappeared down a rabbit hole.

Though Sturdee realised that here was another easy opportunity to thwart the royal hunter, he had made up his mind he was not going to deprive him of his hard-won prize, so he left the wounded and petrified rabbit to its imminent fate, despite the sure knowledge that the animal's manner of death would not be as merciful and swift as the one he might choose to deliver. But, he pondered, that was often Nature's way, and always had been, ever since the dawn of the first predators aeons ago, and what right had he to interfere? He knew of some shooters who, had they witnessed such a rare event as he had just done, would have lain in wait for the royal hunter to return to his prey and then shot him.

For almost the whole of the last week the bitch stoat Aella had been confined to her den in the roof space of Southfield Mill House. There she had laid up a cache of mice, rats and birds to tide her over a period when she needed to conserve her energy, for it had been the time of the winter moult. The shortening days of winter and the sudden onset of cold weather had triggered off changes in her body that brought about the rapid growth of dense white fur beneath her ruddy-brown summer coat, a process that used up a great deal of energy.

Four days previously her tail, as far as the black tassel, her flanks and the outsides of her legs, beginning with her feet, gradually turned white as the old coat moulted to expose the winter one growing through beneath. Over the following three days the white fur had extended up the sides of her body to cover her entire back and finally her head, leaving a ring of brown fur round each eye and a tiny patch on the tip of her muzzle. The old fur that was shed had become incorporated into the warm lining of the nest, which Aella had felted with the fur and feathers of her prey.

Now, at the end of the fourth day, even the rings of brown hairs around her eyes and the patch on her muzzle had been shed, and she wore a coat of winter ermine, whose white hairs were suffused with pale yellow, as if she had run through a field of buttercups. But the long, glossy black hairs of the tail tassel remained, and contrasted strongly against the rest of the tail and body, just like the ermine pelts that were once used in their hundreds to trim the state robes of monarchs and peers of the realm.

Though Aella's sister also wore ermine, her three surviving brothers did not, and had only moulted into thicker winter coats, whose dense grey underfur showing through the longer, brown guard hairs gave the animals a lighter, slightly ragged, look. It was only usual in cold northern climes for the dog stoat, as well as the bitch, to change into ermine. But during the time of the Ice Age, all stoats hunting on the snow-covered wold would have worn ermine to enable them to stalk their prey undetected, and also to help conceal them from predators such as the great white owl and Arctic fox. Aella's body had retained in its genes a memory of those far-off times.

When she emerged from the eaves of the house it was a bright moonlight Christmas Eve. She climbed down the creeper, and as she passed a window she was attracted by the bright lights and colours inside the lounge, where a large log fire blazed. She saw the Christmas tree with its dazzling decorations and gaily wrapped presents hanging from its branches and laid out around it, and three children quietly reading or playing. She stood up on her hindlegs on the stone windowsill and began to paw the pane, moving her head from side to side in the manner of a cat eyeing its prey and frisking her handsome tail. Then she started to tap her head against the glass.

One of the children heard the strange sounds and looked up from her book to see the sinuous, white shape at the window, which at first she thought was a friend's lost ferret, and she called to her brothers to come and look. Then the children recognised the royal hunter with the black-tipped brush they had seen dashing around trying to catch birds on the lawn back in the autumn, but they couldn't understand why, instead of being brown and white, she was wearing white all over. They peered closely at the stoat and marvelled at her beautiful, thick, soft-looking fur, the long guard hairs standing erect in response to the cold air and glistening like gossamer in the moonlight. They saw the dark, piercing eyes and pricked ears, the velvet-like muzzle with its little depressions from which sprouted long, white, swept-back whiskers, the delicate pink tongue licking the glass and the tiny sharp teeth gleaming like porcelain from the open mouth, whose breath condensed in a fine haze on the glass.

Aella lifted a forepaw and pressed it against the pane, so that the children could see the tiny pads and sharp claws with thick white fur growing between them. They longed to open the window and let the stoat in, but although the children were used to keeping all manner of pets, their father advised them that it would not be fair to invite such a wild and free animal as the royal hunter into the household. With regret, the children watched as Aella jumped down from the sill on to the sparkling surface of the frosted snow and cantered off in the direction of the brook, almost blending into the whiteness of the garden except for the bobbing of her black tail tag.

She ran over the hard snow that covered all but the tallest tussocks in the ancient water meadow, her feet leaving only shallow prints in the crisp crust. After every few bounds she would stop and incline her head, and with pricked ears listen for the tiny sounds made by feeding field voles as they moved around in their surface runs beneath the snow. On several occasions she sensed a vole beneath her feet and dived down through the snow towards the sound, but each time the vole escaped her grasp. Or she would sniff at one of their vents in the snow and patiently wait for a vole to surface, but without success.

Hunting field voles in these wintry conditions was precarious for the royal hunter, and sometimes she had to compete with the more wiry weasel who shared the same territory and who was more ideally suited to hunting voles in their subterranean runs. However, the stoat and its smaller cousin at times benefited one another, for the weasel pursuing a vole through its burrows and surface runs might force it to bolt through one of the vents, and it would be pounced on by a hunting stoat as it escaped at full pelt across the snow to seek a new refuge. In turn, the stoat that bolted a vole from under a log sometimes failed to capture it and would watch it disappear beneath the snow, where it would often end up as the prey of a weasel.

There was also another predator that competed with the stoat and weasel for the field vole, and for which the snow cover made hunting even more difficult. A pair of barn owls had raised a brood in the roof of an old woollen mill along the brook, having reared them on the summer's exploding population of voles in this and adjacent meadows. During the harsh winter of four years earlier, many barn owls had died from the intense cold and failure to find sufficient prey, and this was the first year since then that the birds had returned to the valley. The pair's three surviving young had long since dispersed to more distant hunting grounds in the vale, but the parents still frequented this section of the valley. Since the meadows had been covered in snow, field voles were hard to hunt and the owls depended more on the rats that at night foraged along the brook and around the houses and old mills.

Aella rested in the hollow of a pollard willow, one of five regular dens on her territory, her body curled into a tight ball to conserve heat. Next to her lay the scant remains of a field vole she had caught after almost two hour's hunting and five failed attempts at catching her elusive prey. She awoke, and still feeling hungry she stepped out into the snow to hunt again. A barn owl sitting in the willow tree above noticed her leave her resting place, bobbing its head as it watched the whisk of her black tail tip against the whiteness and listening to the minute sounds of her feet breaking the brittle surface of the snow.

The hungry owl glided down from its lookout, its eyes fixed on the dark, restless form of the royal hunter's tail. Though Aella couldn't hear the beat of the owl's silent wings, she saw their shadow preceding her on the moonlit snow, and she turned to look up as the bird bore down on her with swinging talons at the ready. As she dived through a snowdrift, she felt a sudden jerk on the end of her tail, which had slipped through the grip of the owl's talons. She was safe, and all she had lost was a tuft of long black hairs from her tail tag.

Selsleyhill Farm

XXI

Lance Cordwell looked out of the bedroom window of his house in South Woodchester to see a cloudless blue sky with a thick mist hanging low over the valley bottom. Going downstairs, he noted that the weather glass was still high, and stepping outside he saw the golden weathercock on the church steeple pointing towards Rodborough in the cold, almost imperceptible, easterly breeze. The crisp clear air carried the clear melodious call of a mistle thrush all the way from its song post in an ash tree on Amberley Common. Lance also noted that there was a heavy dew on the lawn, and there hadn't been a frost the previous night.

All these signs told the young countryman that scent would be good for hunting on the wold today. Like a good many locals, Lance was a keen follower of the hunt, both the Duke of Beaufort's, which hunted the high plateau of the wold to the east of the Woodchester valley, and the Berkeley, which hunted mainly in the vale but also came up into the hill country during early spring, when the going became hard for the horses in the clay vale.

This March morning Lance planned to take his young son to his first meet of the Berkeley foxhounds at the Rose and Crown in the neighbouring village of Nympsfield. Since the war the Berkeley had rarely hunted in nearby Woodchester Park, for in this steep valley with its thick woodland it was as difficult for the huntsman to hear his hounds as it was for them to hear him, and virtually impossible to reach them. He also found it hard to keep the pack together, for there were so many foxes in the valley that the hounds would divide into several lots, each on the line of a fox.

Before the war Lance would follow on foot, and sometimes ride with, the Berkeley when they met at Stanleyend Farm, or at Stanley Park, the home of Sir Percival Marling, a keen subscriber to the hunt. Then the hounds would draw Dark Wood and Dingle Wood in North Woodchester, Atcombe Wood in South Woodchester, and Pen Wood and Stanley Wood in neighbouring King's Stanley.

When the hunt met at Woodchester Park the hounds would draw Marmontsflat Wood, Break-heart-hill Wood and Collier's Wood. Now all these famous coverts were sanctuary for foxes hunted by hounds, but they were certainly no refuge from the hunter's gun, snare or gin trap.

The Berkeley Hunt had a lineage as ancient as that of the Berkeley family, whose first Roger de Berkeley began building the castle in the reign of William the Conqueror. It is said that the Berkeley family was famed for its deeds of woodcraft and the chase since the reign of King John. Thomas de Berkeley obtained a grant for his services in the Welsh wars 'to hunt the fox, hare, badger and wild cat, with his dogs, within the King's forest, Mendip and the chase of Kingswood'. At one time the Berkeley hunted the whole of the Cotswolds and the Vale of White Horse. The fifth Earl of Berkeley, Frederick Augustus, even hunted from Berkeley Castle to Charing Cross. The season started at Berkeley, moved on to Nettlebed for a month and then to Gerrards Cross to hunt in the Chilterns, and finally to Cranford in Middlesex to hunt the London country. At all these places the hunt had kennels. Then in stages it returned to Berkeley when the season ended. The Berkeley's then huntsman, Tom Oldacre, once hunted a fox from Scratchwood in Wormwood Scrubs to Kensington Gardens. It was said of this most famous of all huntsmen that he could 'guess a fox to death' when there was little or no scent.

The Berkeley hounds had a reputation for work and courage, were famous fox catchers and keen as mustard. Until the introduction of some of Sir Edward Curre's Welsh blood to many kennels, the Berkeley Castle was probably the loudest to be heard, for it had long contained the same Welsh blood. It is said that in the early days of the famous Berkeley kennel the huntsman had at times brought whelps back from across the Severn and put them out to walk in Gloucestershire, and it was well known that the colouring, cry and style of hunting of the old Fitzhardinge blood were very similar to the hound with the Welsh cross.

Berkeley blood had always been much sought after by other kennels for the improvement of nose and cry. Though the war had seen the running down of the pack, it still contained some of its own Berkeley blood, perhaps traces even reaching back to the kennels of the seventh baron, Henry Fitzhardinge, Lord of Berkeley, who flew his own falcons and hunted his own hounds in the reign of Elizabeth I. There was a large amount of blood from the Duke of Beaufort's hounds at nearby Badminton, some from Lord Henry Bentinck's, and some from Earl Ducie's hounds, which were once kept at Woodchester Park. Later, blood from the Cotswold, Heythrop, Atherstone and Cleveland hounds was introduced. The Cleveland hounds possessed sound feet and good shoulders to cope with the disused iron workings of that hilly county. Such qualities benefited the Berkeley hounds when hunting the rough hills of the wooded wold.

As the Woodchester church clock chimed eleven, the hunt assembled in the bright sunshine outside the Rose and Crown at Nympsfield. Bespectacled Captain Berkeley, the master, on his grey mare, huntsman and whipper-in, drunk from their glasses of warming claret cup. Each wore the yellow plush coat that was the ancient hunting dress of the earls of Berkeley, unlike some members of the field who wore the traditional scarlet or hunting pink, which stood out at an even greater distance in the hunting field.

Surrounding the huntsman and his whipper-in was a pack of seventeen and a half couple of foxhounds, fifteen and a half of which were bitches, the rest dog hounds, as different in colour as in personality, and bred for their brains rather than for their looks. Though a few more handsome ones were tan and white with black markings, or tan and black with white legs, throat and tail, most were pies of various hues of black or tan, which were sometimes known as magpie, hare and badger pie. All were of uniform size, powerfully built and displaying that perfect combination of intelligence, muscle, bone and teeth that made them the ideal hunters of foxes. Each had a fine, alert, broad-browed head with triangular ears and long muzzle borne on a long muscular neck, a deep rib cage of well sprung ribs, lean, slightly curved back, and tail, or stern, that was wide at the root and tapering with a graceful curve over the back. Buttocks, loins and thighs were as muscular as those of the huntsman's mount, and lower hindlegs and hocks as slender and sinewy. Shoulders were broad and forelegs straight with elbows set square. Each hound stood on cat-like feet, whose strong nails were kept short and whose pads were toughened by daily exercise on miles of road. Many of the smooth-haired hounds bore scars on their heads and bodies, most left from wounds made by barbed wire, and a few on their muzzles from being bitten by their quarry.

While the majority of the pack were waiting in patient anticipation of the huntsman and whipper-in moving off to hunt, three couples were investigating myriad scents on the grass, and another couple and a half were enjoying being fussed by some foot followers. A five-season, sixty-five pound bitch called Emma had jumped up and laid her large paws on the shoulders of Lance Cordwell's young son. The boy wondered at the hound's sleek, white head with its velvety, cream-coloured ears and brown, soulful, stag-like eyes outlined in black. He stroked her soft, grey-flecked muzzle with its great, moist, pink nostrils, and he looked right down into the hound's open mouth to see the large teeth, especially the two worn canines at the front of the lower jaw. Little did the boy know that many times this gentle hound had used her powerful jaws to snap the neck of a beaten fox with a force of several hundred pounds. Nor did he realise that the large, crescent-shaped scar across the top of her muzzle had been made by the canines of one of those foxes. But from an early age the boy had never been shielded from the sight of death in the countryside, for he knew his father hunted rabbits with a gun, and his father's friends, like Sturdee Click, used ferrets to bolt them from their buries. And only recently he had seen the headless corpses of a neighbour's chickens that a fox had killed in their run.

Suddenly, at a quiet command from the huntsman, the hound jumped down from the boy's shoulders and ran with the others to join the rest of the pack. The hounds bunched up close to the whipper-in's and huntsman's horses, eager to move off, their raised sterns wagging excitedly, for they knew they were about to be taken to draw a nearby covert. The whipper-in led the way down the road in front of the huntsman, trailing his braided white Fitzhardinge whip, ensuring that no hound passed his horse. Behind the huntsman rode the master, accompanied by the hunt secretary, and behind him the owner of the first covert to be drawn. Then came the field, senior and more seriously minded members in front, followed by farmers and riders from every walk of life, with youngsters from the local pony club taking up the rear. Some distance behind walked some of the foot followers, the rest, including Lance and his son, having already taken to the roads in their cars, Land Rovers and motor cycles, to get ahead of the hunt so they could follow its progress from some high vantage point.

At the end of the road the whipper-in led the hounds through a gate held open by a farmhand on to a track that led to the wood where the huntsman intended to make his first draw. The track followed the side of a steep valley made up of stone-walled fields and copses and flanked on its northern side by a one-and-a-half-mile-long stretch of woodland (Bowlas Wood and High Wood), which had always been a stronghold for foxes. Through the bottom of the valley ran a stream fed by springs which issued from the junction of the Cotswold sand and clay, as in the neighbouring valley of Woodchester Park.

As it was well into March the huntsman knew that some vixens might already have dropped their cubs and would be nursing them underground, so the earthstoppers had been informed to block only the main earths, and leave any that looked as if they had been freshly drawn out by a vixen. It was customary for earths to be stopped late at night in all coverts to be drawn, when the foxes had left them, the day before the hunt, and then opened up again after it had finished. The huntsman also knew that the dog foxes had an even chance of escaping the hounds by going to ground in an unstopped earth or a badger set, unless he decided that any of these should be dealt with by the terrier men.

The huntsman had a great respect for the fox, in the same way that the Anglo-Saxon fox-hunters revered their quarry. He like any follower of the hunt was not driven by blood lust. His satisfaction was to be found in seeing his hounds follow their natural instincts in hunting as a well ordered pack, a quarry which, if it were unlucky enough to be outrun and killed, would suffer a death more swift even than many found in Nature. And if it was not caught, it would survive to live another season, if it did not die before from some other cause.

As for resorting to shooting, snaring, trapping, gassing or poisoning of foxes, these methods the huntsman found despicable and unsportsmanlike. On one occasion his hounds had killed a beaten fox only after a short run, and when he had cracked his whip and called the hounds off, he found the wretched animal had a snare round its neck that had cut deep into its flesh. It was a complete bag of skin and bone. Another time a fox crawled out of a ditch right into the mouths of the pack, dragging its maggot-ridden, gangrenous hindlegs, which had been peppered with lead shot.

Beneath a bramble brake halfway up Bowlas Wood a large three-season dog fox lay sleeping in the sun, a short distance from his earth, which he had found stopped after returning to it from a night hunting and patrolling his territory. Nearby lay his pregnant vixen, who had drawn out her den from an old rabbit stop, after digging out and killing the doe and her four month-old kittens. The dog fox still wore his prime winter coat of dense underfur and long, light red outerfur, the hairs of which stood almost erect and which disguised his slight though muscular frame. His slim, spatular, white muzzle was tucked into his light grey loins and rested on his bushy, white-tipped brush, which was folded around him.

The large, black-tipped ears on his broad, wedge-shaped head occasionally twitched as he heard the huntsman's horn in the distance. But as there was no sound of hounds he didn't stir. Before he had reached his first winter he had been hunted by the Duke of Beaufort's hounds, and during the two seasons that he had resided in Berkeley country, he had eluded the hounds by his stealth and speed. Centuries of being hunted had sharpened the natural cunning of these long-legged foxes of the wold, enabling them to perform wonderful feats of skill, daring and resource when being pursued by a pack of hounds.

The whipper-in was the first to arrive at the covert side, ahead of the hounds and huntsman. It was his duty to obey the huntsman, anticipate his every wish, and help him catch his fox. He set his horse well away from the side of the covert where he could see without being seen by a fox, and where he could keep a constant watch for one to go away. The hounds raced on ahead of the huntsman, and when they had all reached the covert side they spread out, waiting expectantly for the signal to go in. The huntsman waited for every hound to get its nose down, for some always took longer than others. He noted that the wind had picked up and was blowing towards the pack along the length of Bowlas Wood, and he knew that he should put hounds in at the bottom of the wood because they would draw and try uphill much better than downhill.

Then with a 'Lieu in there my beauties', he threw the hounds into covert. Without a murmur they worked their way through the wood, diligently scouring the undergrowth, their hackles up and their sterns curled over their backs, every nose sniffing the leaf litter to select the scent of fox from that of badger, stoat, rabbit, squirrel and bird. 'Yoi try,' called the huntsman quietly, encouraging some of the young hounds who had only been entered that season, and had to learn from older, more experienced, hounds.

The dog fox woke and sat up, scratched his red ruff with his hindleg, turned his head, with ears pricked, and looked into the sun through amber eyes with narrow, cat-like pupils towards the bottom of the wood. He had heard a dry twig crack under a hoof of the huntsman's horse, and he was gone as swiftly and silently as a cat. The vixen too was alerted and followed her mate for a short distance before going to ground in the enlarged rabbit stop.

The hounds cast wide and Diplomat, a four-season stallion hound, was the first to settle on the line of the dog fox, who had left his scent behind as soon as he had been unkennelled. The hound gave an excited whimper and wagged his stern vigorously, and the huntsman knew Diplomat had found. Then Friendly, a four-season badger pye bitch, found where the vixen had been kennelled. The two hounds' whimpers grew to a deep baying sound, to which the other hounds gradually added their varyingly pitched voices, and the whole pack, with a great crescendo of music, crashed through the wood in full cry, on the breast-high scent trail of their quarry.

Half a mile ahead of the hounds the fleet-footed fox ran the long covert, mobbed by jays, magpies and carrion crows. The foot followers watching from the road could tell the progress of the fox and hounds in the wood by the pigeons and pheasants that flew out from the treetops. Lance and his son had walked from the ridge road called Tinkley Lane across the fields to High Wood, the next wood to Bowlas Wood, and were waiting at the edge of the covert. From knowledge of former hunts in the area, Lance reckoned the fox would break cover on this side of the wood.

Then, sure enough, he and his son saw a handsome dog fox emerge noiselessly from the brambles, pause to look askance at them, then race down the side of the wood on legs that hardly seemed to touch the ground, the wind blowing against his beautiful brush and so carrying his tail scent with him. Lance lifted his cap to signal to the whipper-in that a fox had broken cover, and the whipper-in gave a high-pitched 'holloa' to tell the huntsman that a fox had gone away. The wily fox's instinct was to try to put the hounds off his scent by running downwind, for this ploy, along with his superior speed, gave him a good head start on his pursuers.

With a sudden loud burst of music the hounds came tumbling out of the wood, and just as suddenly, as they came to a check, they began to hunt mute, busily casting around on the grass for their quarry's scent, which had now eluded their great nostrils and panting, tongue-lolling mouths. Some hounds ran alongside the covert into the wind, a short distance before turning back in a semicircle, others ran out into the field before returning to the spot where the fox broke covert, while some of the young entry stood around waiting for their huntsman to arrive. Several, led by a six-season stallion hound called Rallywood, ran in the direction the fox had gone. Rallywood's whimper was the signal to the rest of the pack that he had picked up the faint scent left by the fox's pads on the grass. Then his deep-throated howl showed he had found the stronger, sweet tail scent floating breast high above it, and as their huntsman blew 'Gone away' on his horn, the pack chimed up and spoke to the fox's line, the whipper-in following in the rear, encouraging a few stragglers forward on to their huntsman.

The vixen slept in the den she had prepared for the birth of her cubs, oblivious that her mate was being pursued by hounds. Neither had she any concern that, should he be killed by them, she would have no help in procuring food for herself and her family while they were confined to the nursery. The previous March he had been hunted while paired with the same vixen, but had returned to perform his paternal duties. Like all animals, the fox lived for the moment. Though no huntsman could deny that when the hunting season opened in the autumn, the vixen became very concerned for the welfare of her well-grown offspring and often lost her life in the endeavour to protect them. Towards the end of the season, the huntsman of the Berkeley was well aware that the hounds might get on the line of a pregnant vixen, even though it was said she carried no scent while in that condition, and wherever possible he would whip off the hounds to save her.

The dog fox had almost half a mile start on the hounds. He ran obliquely across the wind down the hillside into the valley, leaping over stone walls and squeezing through hedges by familiar runs. At the stream he stopped to cool his pads and quench his thirst, and he heard the baying hounds gaining on him. Though his speed and cunning gave him an initial advantage over his hunters, he hadn't the superior stamina that their muscle and fine fare gave them. He made for Slidden's covert where he knew there were earths, but when he arrived at one he regularly used he found it stopped, and he knew there was not enough time to try for others. The hounds came to a check where he had gone into the stream. Some couldn't resist paddling and drinking the cool, clear spring water, but when the huntsman and whipper-in arrived, the hounds knew that they should not dally but help the rest of the pack to pick up the fox's line.

The fox decided to make for some earths in Owlpen Wood, on the other side of the road to Wotton-under-Edge. But when he arrived at the roadside wall he saw a line of vehicles belonging to hunt followers, and their waving arms and excited 'holloas' made him change his mind and stick to the country he knew best, so reluctantly he turned upwind, knowing this would give the hounds an advantage. The followers too had a great respect for the fox, and none of them wished to see him killed by the hounds, and one, thinking that he was tired because he was panting, shouted, 'Go on, Charlie, you can make it.'

When the pack left Slidden's covert and entered the field the fox had crossed to reach the road, they had difficulty owning the line and slowed their pace, for the grass was foiled by the manure of sheep that had recently been grazing there. But with some encouragement from the huntsman, the bitch hounds Pitiful and Emily puzzled out the line and led the pack on the same left-handed turn the headed fox had made, running with greater determination, for the wind carried their quarry's tail scent to them, even though it was beginning to weaken, as was characteristic of a fox that had been hunted for more than a mile or so.

As a result of the hounds' latest check, the fox had gained some distance on them, but he knew he must try and get out of the wind and make for the security of the wood. He ran back down into the valley, crows diving down to mob him as he once more made for the stream. Here he took a field vole by surprise that was basking in its run among the rank waterside grass, and ate it at his leisure before continuing along one of his familiar paths into Bowlas Wood. Once inside the wood he moved with purpose, for he knew where another dog fox would be kennelled. He stopped and turned to listen to the hounds as they entered the wood on his fading scent trail, and ran up an inclined, partly uprooted beech tree as nimbly as a squirrel or stoat. The previous season he had used the same tree as a refuge from the chase.

Lying stretched out along a branch, he watched the hounds gather round the base of the tree, trying to puzzle out the line. But they did not linger long, for Emma gave a whimper nearby, and soon the whole pack was speaking to the line of another fox. The fresh scent stirred the hounds into a chorus that resonated through the wood. The huntsman was so attuned to his hounds, and could even distinguish individual voices, that he could tell by the urgency of their cries that they had unkennelled another fox.

From past experience Lance guessed that the first fox the hounds had hunted was a ringing one that would return to the covert, so he and his son waited at the edge of the wood hoping to see the hounds push out another fox, for Bowlas Wood and High Wood were always full of foxes at this time of year. Father and son heard the cry of the hounds approaching the top of the wood. A jay gave its harsh 'skaaak, skaaak' cry, and a dog fox dashed out, turning downwind in the same direction the first fox had gone. Lance holloaed to let the huntsman and whipper-in know that another one had gone away, which he noticed was a sickly looking animal that seemed to be running with a limp. The hounds streamed out of the wood and immediately got on his line. Though passing close to Lance and his son, they took not the slightest notice of them, for all their senses were so concentrated on running down their quarry. The young boy fancied that he recognised the bitch hound Emma whom he had fondled at the meet, and he saw in her a different kind of animal.

After going some distance the fox smelled the foot scent left by the hounds on their first run, and he turned across the wind to head for the road, with the hounds, led by Clara and Emma, in hot pursuit. The majority of the foot followers had left in their vehicles for the Wotton road to watch the first run, so there were few in Tinkley Lane to head the fox. Instead of crossing straight over the lane it ran up the middle for some distance, before clumsily leaping up on to the drystone wall that enclosed Woodchester Park. It stood for a moment looking down the lane to watch the hounds come to a check, then jumped down into the field.

The hounds ran up and down the road and grass verge trying to feel for the line. A six-season stallion hound called Deputy, who had the best nose in the pack to discern a fox's scent from the foil of tarmac and oil of cars and farm tractors, feathered up the middle of the road, his powerful stern lashing from side to side. His sudden whimper and dash over the wall where the fox had gone confirmed to the huntsman reynard's ruse, and soon the rest of the pack were scrambling over the wall on to his line.

The lame fox ran over Lynch Knoll and down the steep hillside into the valley, the hounds running hard and gradually gaining on him. He had been hunted before, and he knew by the hounds' cry that his scent was strong. He must find an open earth to save his life. The hindleg that had recently been broken by a glance from a speeding car was giving him increasing pain. The lead hounds broke from scent to view and their cry changed to the higher note of running for the kill.

Now Diplomat took the lead from Deputy and ran several lengths ahead. The fox began to feel his strength ebb. He could no longer sustain the pace, even though the going was all downhill. He reached the valley bottom and began to twist and turn in a last desperate effort to thwart his pursuers. He passed the old kennels where Lord Ducie once kept his own pack of hounds, among which were famous stallion hounds like Berkeley Nathan and Rocket.

Diplomat was turning short with his quarry and running hard at his brush. When within only a few bounds of Kennel Pond and the safety of its reedy margin, the fox felt a blow on his flank as the heavy hound crashed into him, winding him and knocking him off his feet. Lying on his back, he lunged at Diplomat with jaws snapping wildly. He saw the hound's bloodshot eyes and great jaws open wide, but hardly felt their powerful and fatal grip round his neck.

In an instant the fox went limp and the pack began to break up his corpse, so that by the time the huntsman arrived to find the hounds' muzzles smeared with blood, only one of his pads, his brush and part of his mask remained. The huntsman sounded several sharp, tremulous blasts on his horn to tell the field that the hounds had made a kill. Near the very same spot in the park Berkeley Nathan had killed a fox more than a century before.

The Tower, Woodchester Park

XXII

In his treetop den in Break-heart-hill Wood Aethelbeorht had heard the baying of the hounds re-echoing through the valley, as he had heard the distant death rattle sounded on the huntsman's horn. He lay curled up in the warm, moss-lined winter drey of a grey squirrel built in the fork of an oak tree, which stood close to the stone tower that Earl Ducie had built for his family and guests to observe the progress of his hounds when hunting in the park. Aethelbeorht had taken over the breeding drey after killing and eating the young, helpless squirrels inside. Now that spring had almost arrived the young dog stoat was becoming restless. He was fast reaching adulthood, and the longer, sunnier days aroused in him a desire to explore the country beyond the park, where he could seek new territory and bitch stoats to mate with, just as his father Aethelwald had done before him.

As the Berkeley huntsman and whipper-in lifted the hounds to draw another covert beyond the park, Aethelbeorht emerged from the squirrel's drey and climbed down the tree head first, carefully feeling for footholds in the rugged bark. He ran along a ride through the wood into adjoining Colepark Wood, mobbed by titmice and blackbirds and almost running into a surprised fox, which had been disturbed from its sleep by the recent cries of the hounds. He stopped to drink some stagnant rainwater, which had collected in a hollow at the base of a tree, and he recognised the scent mark of an older dog stoat that had established its territory in the wood. Every time he came across the scent he felt insecure and now he had an urge to put the park behind him.

He left the wood by a well-used run and crossed pasture known as Fish Pool Ground, skirting the two fish ponds where carp were once fattened for the Ducie's table. In the cover of a drystone wall he ran over a field called Yew Ground, where rooks were probing the grass for fat grubs and worms to take to their brooding mates that were nesting in one of the many elm tree rookeries. One bird chased him a short distance, half hopping, half flying, and tried to peck at his flourishing tail tag. Aethelbeorht stopped in his tracks and hissed at the rook through bared teeth, then galloped on, crossing Shankcombe and Road Piece before finding sanctuary in Terrats Bank Wood.

The next few days he spent hunting and resting in the wooded combe in which lay Atcombe Court. In the stream that ran through the park grounds he killed a trout, diving into the water and catching it and bringing it ashore to eat, as adept as his close cousin the otter, which also sometimes frequented the stream, especially when the fish came upstream to spawn and when eels were running. In Atcombe Wood he searched the trees for the early clutches of mistle thrushes and hunted a grey squirrel with all the prowess of his arboreal ancestors. He came across the squirrel as it searched for the autumn acorns it had buried in the grass of the park a short way out from the wood. He watched from behind a tree stump as it scented and dug for acorns, in between stopping to scan the woodland floor for signs of danger. The squirrel's wide field of vision, its ability to perceive the slightest movements, and its exceptional power of focusing over great distances, made it the royal hunter's most challenging quarry.

Aethelbeorht knew that he could not stalk the squirrel over the grass without the concealment of cover, so he waited for it to return to the wood. He watched it run up an oak tree and sit on a branch to eat an acorn. He stalked through the flowering dog's mercury to the foot of the tree, rose on his hindlegs, reaching up to his fullest height, and began to climb slowly up the straight, branchless trunk, making sure to keep himself hidden from the squirrel's view. The squawk of a sharp-eyed jay betrayed him and made him freeze in his steps. The squirrel heard the bird's warning cry and stopped skinning the acorn, its eyes scanning the tree and the ground below for signs of danger.

Aethelbeorht reached the first branch and pulled himself up on to it by his forelegs. A tiny piece of falling acorn husk glanced one of the sensitive vibrissae on his head, and he looked up to see the squirrel on the branch above. The eagle-eyed squirrel spied the royal hunter and gave its sharp, chattering alarm cry while jerking its erect bushy tail. Aethelbeorht made a sudden spring at the squirrel and chased it up the tree and along one of its spreading branches, never more than a few feet behind.

So agile was the royal hunter that the woodmen from nearby Workman's sawmills, who were extracting timber from the wood with their team of four, at first thought they were seeing two squirrels chasing one other. The squirrel ran to the end of the branch and jumped several feet on to the branch of a neighbouring tree. Aethelbeorht followed, gripping the slender end of the branch between his pads and claws, his bushed-out tail gyrating to balance himself, and hesitantly leapt across a gap of several feet, almost missing his foothold on the branch as it recoiled from the squirrel's leap.

A cacophony of birds' cries warned every creature in the wood as Aethelbeorht pursued the squirrel from branch to branch and up and down the tree trunk, the squirrel continually letting out its clucking distress calls. Occasionally both animals halted, each out of sight of the other on opposite sides of the trunk. Aethelbeorht detected the movements of the squirrel by its intermittent calls and the noise its claws made on the bark, and the squirrel with its superior hearing relied solely on the minute sounds made by Aethelbeorht's claws.

The squirrel moved broadside round the trunk, head uppermost, listening out for the royal hunter. Aethelbeorht slowly descended the trunk on the opposite side, and following its scent trail over the bark, looked up to see the squirrel clinging motionless to the trunk a few feet away. Summoning all his strength he raced up the trunk and grabbed the squirrel's tail in his jaws. The squirrel turned to face him, barking sharply through its bared chisel-sharp teeth.

Aethelbeorht gained a surer grip on his prey, straddling its body with all four legs whilst trying to avoid its gnashing teeth. The squirrel lost its foothold and both animals fell to the ground. They rolled over in the dead leaves, their squeals and barks once more accompanied by the cries of blackbirds, wrens, titmice and jays. Then Aethelbeorht found the place behind the squirrel's head to bury his canine teeth. The wood became silent again, except for the doleful piping of a hen blackbird and the hollow thuds of axes as the woodmen trimmed the great branches of a felled hundred-year-old beech.

It was starlight when Aethelbeorht left the grounds of Atcombe Court and made for the land on the other side of the valley. He followed the brook as far as Church Mill and swam across the water to the place where a stream from the opposite hillside, flowing through a culvert beneath road and railway, joined the brook. He ran through the dark culvert, leaving his scent mark on stones close to those of other stoats that used the same route, until he emerged by Little Britain Farm. Countless generations of royal hunters and other members of the weasel tribe had used these same watercourses long before man culverted them to build his roads and railways across them. They had always been constant landmarks for migratory mammals, and where the flow of water through the culvert was too great for the animal to get through, it would make a risky road crossing close to the site of the hidden stream.

Aethelbeorht now found himself on unfamiliar ground, in one of the wooded combes below Rodborough. He followed the stream through the combe until he reached a large fish pond which, it is thought, originated as a clay pit used by the Romans to produce bricks and tiles for the villa at Woodchester. He listened to the croaking of many frogs that were spawning in the shallow water at the reedy edge of the pond. The unusual sound awakened his curiosity and appetite, and he entered the spawn-filled water, grabbed an egg-filled female by one of its hindlegs and pulled it to the shore squealing. Within the space of fifteen minutes he had bitten the heads off ten frogs, skinned their hindlegs and stripped them of their sweet, white flesh, leaving the rest of their bodies untouched.

The squeals of the frogs had alerted a tawny owl perching in a beech several hundred yards away on the edge of the escarpment. Aethelbeorht heard the owl's sharp 'kewick' as it reassured its mate, a call he had heard many times during his stay in Woodchester Park, and one that always made him wary when he was out hunting at night. He decided to distance himself from the owl's calls and continue up the combe under cover of the stream's bank to its spring source just below a beech wood. As he was about to enter the wood he saw the dark, silent form of a tawny owl drop down from a tree, and he froze in his tracks. He heard a squeak as the owl's sharp talons pierced the quivering body of a wood mouse, and watched the owl carry it off to its mate.

As the sun came up over the wold, Aethelbeorht stirred from his short slumber in a rabbit hole in Conygre Wood, below Stroud Hill. Since the early hours he had travelled almost four miles from Rodborough Common, down Butter Row, crossing railway, canal, river and road in the Golden Valley, and had picked up a stream flowing through a steep combe that brought him high up on to the wold. He ate some more of the full-grown buck rabbit it had taken him half an hour to kill, being almost four times his own weight. With such a large store of fresh flesh near at hand he had no need to hunt for a few days, so he curled up close to his prey and slept through the rest of the morning.

Soon after midday Aethelbeorht woke to the sound of a hunting horn and the baying of hounds. The Vale of White Horse hounds, which the Earl of Ducie hunted more than a century ago, had met at nearby Lypiatt Park that morning and were hunting in woodland at the head of Toadsmoor Valley. Youthful Lauree Lee, a mile and a half away in the garden of his Slad home, also heard the huntsman's horn and delighted in its sound, as he did when the neighbouring Cotswold hounds drew Worgan's Wood close to his cottage.

Aethelbeorht heard the hounds getting closer, and as they rushed into Coneygre Wood on the scent of their fox, he felt the reverberations through the burrows of the warren from their two hundred feet and from the pounding hooves of the huntsman's and whipper-in's horses. He also heard the loud baying of the hounds round the fox's earth, then the huntsman's cry of 'whoo-hoop' and the soft, mournful note he blew on his horn to inform the field that their fox had gone to ground.

Aethelbeorht had been in the area almost a week before he discovered Lypiatt Park. The park had its origins in Anglo-Saxon and Norman times, when part of the forest was enclosed by a fence or palisade of cleft-oak stakes to prevent the escape of the wild deer, which provided game for hunting and a supply of fresh meat for winter use. Deer were even driven into the enclosure from outside. The name of the park is said to be derived from a gate in the fence, a so-called 'leap gate', in front of which was a ramp of soil and turf, which the deer could leap over when being driven into the enclosure, but which kept them in because of a ditch along the inside of the fence. Now the park and the surrounding woodland were used for rearing pheasants, as it had been for more than a hundred years. In its heyday, before the Great War, the estate had employed a number of gamekeepers, whose job it was to rear pheasants for shooting and to protect the birds and their eggs from predators such as stoats, weasels, foxes, hedgehogs, hawks and crows by trapping, snaring and shooting.

Each spring and summer, as dog stoats ranged widely in search of new territory and mates, many were attracted by the plentiful supply of the eggs and young of pheasants, as well as by the strong scent of bitch stoats in season that were not already with young from matings the previous summer. The keeper, who was well acquainted with the stoat's most intimate habits, knew that once he had caught a bitch, he could be sure to catch many dog stoats in the same trap by squeezing out her urine and the contents of her scent glands and smearing them over the trap.

Like many of these dog stoats, Aethelbeorht was oblivious of the wiles of the gamekeeper, for so far his life had been spent in country that was not keepered. In Ferris Gate Covert he saw the corpses of trapped animals that the keeper had hung by their necks to a gibbet. Apart from a few freshly killed stoats and weasels, there were many that had been trapped the previous summer, their shrivelled, maggot-consumed bodies often only recognisable by the presence or absence of black-tipped tails. There were also several grey squirrels and hedgehogs and the shrunken, feathered forms of jays, magpies and carrion crows, a tawny owl and a sparrowhawk, all predators of the keeper's precious birds or their eggs.

More than a hundred years ago kites would have shared the keeper's gibbet, for then these birds were common over the combes, as place names like nearby Kitlye signified. But despite the gamekeeper's readiness to kill predators of game, he maintained a healthy estate by his management of the pheasant coverts, and by his careful control of predators that preyed on the eggs and young of songbirds as well as those of partridges and pheasants.

In order to trap stoats and weasels the gamekeeper relied on the animals' insatiable curiosity for exploring holes. He would set a gin trap, pegged down well in the ground, in a wooden tunnel or drainage pipe covered with turves, and disguise every part, including the pan, jaws, spring and chain, with a thin covering of soil and leaves. The tunnels and traps were sited at the ends of hedges and drystone walls where there was a gap or a gate, and for the deadliest results, on a plank across a stream or ditch, in the vicinity of the rearing field and the coverts where the young pheasant poults were later penned out. The gamekeeper would check the traps first thing in the morning and late in the evening so as to prevent needless suffering to an animal not killed instantly but only caught.

One night Aethelbeorht was hunting round a wood on the estate known as Pheasant Covert. Many times he stopped to deposit his scent close to the scent marks of other dog stoats that were running, and at one of them beneath a tree he lingered longer, for besides the scent of a bitch stoat in season, there was also another that seemed familiar to him. From its freshness he could tell that he was close to its owner. Then he heard a rapid high-pitched clucking sound above his head, and he looked up to see another dog stoat standing on a branch, his ears laid back and teeth bared, hackles up and tail nervously twitching. Aethelbeorht shrunk back in surprise and cackled loudly in reply.

A tawny owl watched and listened unseen from the same tree and swivelled its head to focus eyes and ears on the stoats as they wrestled with one another in the undergrowth. Both royal hunters were engaged in a contest over the same bitch stoat whose scent they had been following. Grasping one another by their forelegs they rolled over and over down the wood bank, chattering angrily, unaware that the small bitch stoat they were fighting over had just been taken in the talons of the tawny owl.

Aethelbeorht bit a piece out of his opponent's ear, and both released their hold on one another. The defeated dog stoat ran off down the ditch, watched by Aethelbeorht, who no longer felt any kinship for the brother who had also travelled to Lypiatt from Woodchester. Later that night when Aethelbeorht investigated one of the gamekeeper's tunnels and sniffed at the still warm corpse crushed by the powerful steel jaws of the gin trap, he felt no remorse for his brother, and quickly resumed the patrol of his new-found domain.

Back in South Woodchester, as March gave way to April, Aethelbeorht's only surviving sister, Aella, felt changes coming over her body that only bitch stoats with young can feel. In less than a week she had moulted her white winter coat of ermine and had grown back her glossy ruddy-brown pelt, so that when the children from Southfield Mill House caught a fleeting glance of her in the garden one morning, they had no idea it was the same little royal hunter they had seen in the snow last Christmas Eve.

Although Aella had spent most of the winter in the roof space of the old house, over the last month she had used a cavity in the drystone wall that enclosed the garden as her main den. In it she had made a nest of dried grass lined with the fur of water voles and feathers of moorhens she had caught along the nearby brook. For ten months she had carried the latent germs of six new lives in her womb, until they became implanted as the first celandines came into flower along the banks of the brook. Only during the beginning of this the eleventh month, since the embryos had been rapidly growing, did she feel her slim belly swell and her tiny teats fill out in preparation for the birth of her young. She lay curled up in her warm nest, her beautiful head tucked into her white loins and her lustrous, black-tipped brush wrapped around her, listening to the beating of six tiny hearts.